Humorous Cryptograms

300 Large Print Puzzles To Keep You Entertained

By: Game Nest

gamenest.org

This book is dedicated to all Cryptogram lovers across the globe. Whether you are a beginner or expert, these puzzles will provide hours of entertainment!

If you enjoy the book, please consider leaving a review wherever you bought it.

ISBN: 978-1-951791-53-7

Get All Our New Releases For FREE!

Sign up to our VIP Newsletter to get
all of our
future releases absolutely free!

www.gamenest.org/free

Contents

Welcome! This book contains 300 cryptographic puzzles containing funny quotes… but it's up to YOU to crack the codes!

Cryptography can be traced back 4,000 years to the use of hieroglyphs by the Egyptians. Hieroglyphs were a secret language known only to the scribes who used them to transmit messages on behalf of their kings.

A cryptogram is simply a coded message or an encryption. They have also been used for encryption of military or personal secrets as well as for entertainment purposes. There are many other benefits to solving cryptograms and other word puzzles. Solving such puzzles has been shown to help the brain by improving memory, vocabulary, and focus. They also improve pattern recognition which is an important cognitive skill. Additionally, completing a task such as a word puzzle gives us a sense of accomplishment and our brains reward us with a surge of dopamine, the feel-good chemical. And studies have shown that frequent cognitive activity can keep the brain fit as we age.

HOW TO SOLVE

The cryptograms in this guide are substitution puzzles where each letter of the alphabet is represented by a different letter. Take a look at the example below.

URGT R FBZT SRK!

is

HAVE A NICE DAY!

CODE:

I N V Y A D E H C

B F G K R S T U Z

B is replaced by I, F is replaced by N, etc.

Your task is to figure out the code to solve each puzzle.

<u>TIPS</u>

The best tip is to **use a pencil** to keep track of your guesses. Here are instances to look for when you begin solving.

<u>Single letters</u>

One letter words will often be an A or I (or sometimes O).

<u>Contractions</u>

A word with an apostrophe is most likely a contraction, such as

CAN'T, WON'T, DIDN'T, YOU'RE, YOU'LL

The "...N'T" ending is very common.

<u>Double letters</u>

Common double letters are SS, EE, TT, LL, MM, OO, FF, such as in LE<u>TT</u>ER, SU<u>MM</u>ER, and O<u>FF</u>ER.

<u>Common letters or words</u>

Certain letters are used more frequently, such as the letter E. The English alphabet arranged by frequency of use is:

E, T, A, O, I, N, S, H, R, D, L, U, C, W, M, F, Y, G, P, B, V, K, J, X, Q, Z

Last but not least – it's easy to get frustrated if you get stuck on a puzzle. Fear not, we have provided hints on page 107. Complete answers can be found on page 118.

Remember to have fun and enjoy solving these 300 cryptogram puzzles!

CRYPTOGRAMS

1. EQZ ENWFUO SJR WFYWFWER: ENR
CFWLRJOR SFH NCDSF OECGWHWEA; SFH
W'D FZE OCJR SIZCE ENR CFWLRJOR.

                              -SPIRJE RWFOERWF

2. SMGP ZEL PGPH KEXWBPC XSMX
MKZNECZ CHWGWKI FOEYPH XSMK ZEL WF
MK WCWEX, MKC MKZEKP IEWKI RMFXPH
XSMK ZEL WF M JMKWMB?

                              -IPEHIP BMHOWK

7

3. U QWH'C DHWZ ZYBC'N GWTM
MAYBLNCUHV BEWLC SBTMHCUHV: CYM
VMCCUHV LS MBTXP, WT CYM BOCUHV
XUDM PWL DHWZ ZYBC PWL'TM QWUHV.

-RUG VBJJUVBH

4. TNI YQZZNR YNWWVYR QZ NPM
KVWANZ VHVWT RGEV RLVT AQT
ANEVRLGZS NXXVZAGHV. TNI JNIPM
ZVHVW EQBV GR RLWNISL RLQZBASGHGZS
MGZZVW.

-ARVKLVZ YNPUVWR

8

5. VNW LIJP AUP VL SWWB PLZD
NWUJVN CE VL WUV ANUV PLZ XLI'V
AUIV, XDCIS ANUV PLZ XLI'V JCSW,
UIX XL ANUV PLZ'X DUVNWD ILV.

                              -GUDS VAUCI

6. YUC BEE MTGXQMBEL BJG SBR.
IQCTUDC MTGXQMBEL LDMT BL TKRJUZGY
BYR UOKZGY WUJ GOBXNEG, CTGJG
IUDER SG YU IBK CU XBVG IBCGJ, B
AQCBE QYZJGRQGYC QY SGGJ.

                              -RBAG SBJJK

7. TJ XCQI UAG'RO YABO TH HIGVTY
NGI TI XAZEH, ICOB TI ZOQDDU THB'I
ICQI HIGVTY QI QDD.

9

-YQRTY DOIIOZPQB

8. XPMRZP ERY SZVIVSVWP O DOG,
HOKC O DVKP VG NVL LNRPL. INOI
HOE, HNPG ERY QR SZVIVSVWP NVD,
ERY'KK XP O DVKP OHOE OGQ NOTP NVL
LNRPL.

-LIPTP DOZIVG

9. JPVJMP LXA GVWIDGO DL
DHJVLLDEMP, ETW D NV GVWIDGO PFPUA
NXA.

-X. X. HDMGP

10. G YMJ'C FZRP SPC SPPRPU EGAP
UMTP SPMSEP. G FZRP IFMEP APJJPEU
MQ GBBGCZCGMJ.

—IFMMSG WMEYDPBW

11. SDHXGJC OEHWOCM LS STC MHHD,
GXS, TCLDREK JLXKTSCD, TXDDRCM
LULA.

—GCEFLQRE PDLEOJRE

12. UIDINNPWK PN HRIK C KIPQRXWU
GWNIN RPN OWX. FITUINNPWK PN HRIK
LWB GWNI LWBUN.

—UWKCGF UICQCK

13. I GFEIK YR TYVD I JDI CIA —
PFZ NIK'J JDTT XFG RJSFKA RXD YR
ZKJYT PFZ MZJ XDS YK XFJ GIJDS.

—DTDIKFS SFFRDODTJ

14. SV R HPDRJ GCAAU FPY UXC'U
GHCJGF RJO APPIU USKGCCJ, UXC'U
GHCALC. SV UXC GCAAU FPY UXC'U
GHCJGF-USK RJO APPIU GHCJGF-USK,
UXC'U ORDJ JCRM VPMGF.

-EXMSU MPEI

15. ZC KHN RZFY BH UY HEY VNEQTYQ,
KHN'FY WHB ZB JDQY. FYTK CYA
IYHIRY QZY IDPB BVDB DWY.

-WYHTWY UNTEP

12

16. AHKKHG KI GHJYQB XQPHBK YBO AH
KLIWELK Y UIIP KLYB KI XTHYF IWK
YBO GHJISH YPP OIWAK.

-YAGYLYJ PQBDIPB

17. G LPQIMP YX OXGA CAV SNIT YFCY
DXINR FCEP UP CM C UPUTPL.

-WLXISFX UCLH

18. B EBKR VI B LHBWO NDBN ZVHH
HOKG XUT PUKOX VQ XUT WBK LJUMO
NDBN XUT GUK'N KOOG VN.

-EUE DULO

13

19. ZEYN QHXNA CWNIIG YKAI. EY GHD
BHJ'I AIHC KJB ZHHO KWHDJB HJUN EJ
K SVEZN, GHD UHDZB QEAA EI.

                              -RHVJ VDFVNA

20. PU COFBIDPFS TCJBBE AFTZN, WFA
KFYC YFDWCTN FSBE WJOC DAF WJSHN?
                              -YPBDFS QCTBC

21. TP GTA KVXLTW KVWN IRIE'N LPN
NTP ZAOP.   -BTVCKPW IP LVXKKP

22. GEKGDI XQLNPJF DQVL FWFCPFI -
WQUBPWN GWWQDI UBFC IQ CVHB.

                              -QIHGL KPETF

23. OVL CXLJCZL YNZ KM C HKFLJ
RLJMNH OVCH OVL CXLJCZL RLJMNH.

                              -CHYA JNNHLA

24. VH MDHLI RGH KCAMR RVHUQH
PNLRGM NK NWA OGCUIAHL'M UCQHM
RHSOGCLE RGHP RN VSUB SLI RSUB SLI
RGH LHZR RVHUQH RHUUCLE RGHP RN
MCR INVL SLI MGWR WD.

                              -DGTUUCM ICUUHA
25. MOG JY VOSG WNPP BV EIAO OYIE
MOSQ QYVOBQR DYUSA?

                              -EYXBQ MBPPBNDA

26. XZB'D MZOOA GWZFD DJI MZOEX

VZHPBT DZ GB IBX DZXGA. PD PU

GEOIGXA DZHZOOZM PB GFUDOGEPG.

                    -VJGOEIU H. UVJFEK

27. H UZKMQZ OE WBQYZU OVWO

JMZQOHEB EB OVZ LUEMBCQ OVWO H

CEB'O NBEY OVZ WBQYZU.

                    -CEMLIWQ WCWTQ

28. N THC'G XSCG GH SMANJBJ

NFFHPGSRNGW GAPHDQA FW XHPI. N

XSCG GH SMANJBJ NG GAPHDQA CHG

TWNCQ.

                    -XHHTW SRRJC

16

29. TDGDM VBQQBC WTUBTD DQJD'J
XWIN. RTQDJJ UBR'MD LT IND CBBFJ
WTF UBR'MD QBJI WTF UBR JDD W
XWIN. INDT OU WQQ SDWTJ VBQQBC
INWI XWIN.

-DQQDT FDKDTDMDJ

30. YZJUZ RPZ FSFZTR. IZFZFXZI DQQ
RPSYZ GSFZT ST RPZ "RJRDTJK" GPS
GDBZM SVV RPZ MZYYZIR KDIR.

-ZIFD XSFXZKO

31. HF BQFTWSGDJSQD DIKC HX S PGQ
TJGOF GVC S QGSC S PGVD G QXTIVC
IBSVSIV. WX QGSC IZGF, FIY'JX YLKF
DII.

–JICVXF CGVLXJESXKC

32. KJMNGNF ELZA OMPND RLP'V UWD
JLQQZPNEE AZAP'V YPMK KJNFN VM
EJMQ.

—CNFVFWAN EVNZP

33. FTPB Y HYP, Y FMBV VS HYP JYUP
GZ IOMBHWMVTPO FTS HYPH NPMRPWLJJZ
YB TYE EJPPN. BSV EROPMGYBI JYUP
MJJ VTP NMEEPBIPOE YB TYE RMO.

—FYJJ OSIPOE

34. QP EDSJS YSJS OM VNC LSMLIS,
EDSJS YMTIC VS OM RMMC INYASJG.

—FDNJISG CQFXSOG

35. DMUDIH AR SR RSEYT CYRCMY'H
GKQYTDMH, RSEYTUNHY SEYI URQ'S
BRFY SR IRKTH.

                    -IRAN XYTTD

36. X DCF VBXLJXLO CEGQV BGD
ANGAIN FNNW VG MNCP VBN EXEIN C
DBGIN IGV WGMN CF VBNS ONV GIPNM;
VBNL XV PCDLNP GL WN - VBNS'MN
RMCWWXLO ZGM VBNXM ZXLCI NKCW.

                    -ONGMON RCMIXL

37. UWI EHSPU UHLI H PII N GFQQIS
PLHBHXQ, H'BB DFXPHTIS HU.

                    -GFNX SHRISP

38. N'H SNUB GP SNCB SNUB W JPPF

OWQ - PQSI KNGD SPGL PV OPQBI.

-JWXSP JNRWLLP

39. IWEB'X EOTBWKY ITYQ PTY

BWKXECYCX?

-XBKUKO IYDFWB

40. OJDJA QGM BII MSEE MBZBAABC

CNXM FBG LXO PB MNJ PXF XIMJA

MBZBAABC RGYM XY CJEE.

-ZXAT MCXSO

41. QKMC HSC YSWWBSRMH SWM YSGM BZ
KMSNMZ. LAQ HX BH QKAZGMW SZG
IBRKQZBZR.

                    —EIBZQ MSHQFXXG

42. OUNFLZSLP SR U GBQZ. ULI UR U
GBQZ YFYHFN, AJB GUL ZNA ZJ
FKOQUSL SZ ZJ JZXFN OFJOQF, HBZ DF
MBRZ UOOFUN QSTF QBLUZSGR.

                        —MSY PUEESPUL

43. VQ BDX MQ XMZ UPX BK IX
QZDOPBY V'YY DOSOP WROBH KM XMZ
BCBVD.

                    —WKBD YBZPOY

21

44. JLDKD ZMOOUJ YD M ZKWGWG ODBJ
HDDF. EA GZLDVTCD WG MCKDMVA STCC.

                    —LDOKA FWGGWOPDK

45. CV EQDTIXWBE EPJM CD EQD UIV
EP IRQWDFD ETZD WOODT XDIRD WB EP
HWOWBQ UQIE W BEITE. BP HIT W'FD
HWOWBQDM EUP NIYB PH C&CB IOM I
RQPRPJIED RIAD. W HDDJ NDEEDT
IJTDIMV.

                         —MIFD NITTV

46. P OPG JG NQCV JT JGKQOINVWV
XGWJN ZV JT OPSSJVH. WZVG ZV'T
LJGJTZVH.

-BTP BTP UPAQS

47. NVJNWV PI W.F. FEV XVFQBWZ
FKEFPX JK SWCQVI. P HTVFE QJ SJX,
ZJC YJCWX EJA F WPMCJE HQJEV PI
QBPH YPQZ TPQB F AFSVW.

-EZFI EVZIJWXH

48. V BWWD AVQL AVGU, CWFUQVFUC V
UNUG THH VQ QW QLU OWWH.

-A. B. OVUYHC

49. IMK HPVI IKDDXOBXTZ YPDQV XT
IMK KTZUXVM ULTZALZK LDK: X'H ODPH
IMK ZPJKDTHKTI LTQ X'H MKDK IP
MKUS.

-DPTLUQ DKLZLT

50. FHL'Q YZE HAWZ DSCUUWF BCUJ.
NE QRCD QCBW QHBHZZHG, CQ'UU NW
PZWW EHIVZQ.

                        -DQWSRWL YHUNWZQ

51. ZMEIMJ PZM DJ PIMXFRJMW HFWN Z
XVBB NJZR IX NZFU. DVW Z PIMXFRJMW
DZBR GZM - WNJUJ'K EIVU RFZGIMR FM
WNJ UIVCN.

                        -BZUUE RZTFR

52. NGMYVG IYE HUVVI U AGVTYS, IYE
TOYEKR MXVTL HUQG LOGH ETG U
BYHAELGV PXLO TKYP XSLGVSGL LY TGG
POY LOGI VGUKKI UVG.

24

                              —PXKK MGVVGKK

53. C XDUQ TQCLB FOZZCQV. CI'A AD
BZQOI ID JCLV ISOI DLQ AWQRCOX
WQZADL HDE KOLI ID OLLDH JDZ ISQ
ZQAI DJ HDEZ XCJQ.

                              —ZCIO ZEVLQZ

54. F IBW—MYFO WEG TV HTDG WS ETHY
F ZEYDGYO, ZPI MWP GWD'I JFRY FDM
IWA SWO TI.

                              —UYOOM VYTDSYEG

55. CN'X WFSM TPXCTU BEU WT NE
WPQT WPHEU YCBT, WFYNC—WCYYCEV
JEYYPU JTSCXCEVX, NMPV CN CX NE

                    25

JTSCJT EV P SPUOTN BEU WI BUEVN
OEUSM. NMPN'X NMT NUFNM.

—EOUPM ACVBUTI

56. OCQQLCXA LB FVA UVLAD UCGBA MD
ILTMQUA.

—XQMGUVM OCQW

57. G AGXK ASCN ORAXZ, KZTKMGRAAE
OFKC YFKE RVK YRXKC DE TKSTAK OFS
RCCSE HK.

—CSKA MSORVP

58. RG ZKZOW DROGW GIZOZ ROZ GTV
JEQPH VS DZVDBZ - GIVHZ TIV TRQG
GV UV IVCZ RQP GIVHZ TIV PVQ'G.

GIZ GOVANBZ EH, GIZW ROZ AHARBBW
CROOEZP GV ZRLI VGIZO.

                          —RQQ BRQPZOH

59. VEAW F VXR X ZFN HO LXDAWJR
HCUAN X SCJ, KQJ F XSVXOR TCQWN
JEAH.

                          —DCNWAO NXWIADTFASN

60. H JIO'S FZWHZRZ HO DASXIWILM;
H'P D ADLHSSDXHKA DOJ CZ'XZ
AEZTSHNDW.

                          —DXSGKX N. NWDXEZ

61. U PLRLO GLLT SFOL MTFPL KZMP
VZLP U'S KOAUPC KF NYK XYPXEOLLP
FP SA QMEH.

                    −BUSSA HUSSLT

62. JDGTNCCQ KMVO VCMRIV ABQT D
ISDY. BR ZU IDU VTTBRY EBGOMSTV CJ
ETCEATV WDGDOBCRV HDV GCRVBITSTI D
EMRBVPZTRO.

                    −NTOOU HPBOT

63. KVAAWVDH WO UWIH KXOSAPPKO: YH
QPEWNH EPP UVEH WL ESHF VAH DPPZ
PA CVZ.

                    −YPPZF VUUHQ

28

64. CLPEKVPVKAO MPO OAV YF TFRN
LFQZAOQKYRF HAL ZFAZRF HPRRKOC KO
RAEF.

-PRYFLV FKOQVFKO

65. FDIBUXSQF FINF DKLN IBL YRMGY
DR FDIBD EXDDMGY BLPMYMRXF CXRDLF
RG SXEF. DKL TLBN HMBFD RGL OMPP
FIN, "VLFXF! DKMF SXE MF
LZELGFMTL!"

-SRGIG R'UBMLG

66. V LRYIKZSE RBLS TSVZ YS VZ
LCSOO, TKZ DZ JVO BR YVZLC PRE YS
VZ MDLM TRNDBW.

-SYR ICDFDIO

29

67. Z XWZDC GJ RNCH JGQHW LHJLVH
RJWH ZDGHWHPGZDK.

                    —HWDHPG QHRZDKTNI

68. BZ BKZVI ZX TZJ HKZ MIGICOIS
KZAZJMV, QHQMSV QAS SCVBCAGBCZAV,
C VQT HIYY SZAI. QAS BZ BKI G
VBJSIABV, C VQT TZJ, BZZ, GQA RI
EMIVCSIAB ZX BKI JACBIS VBQBIV.

                    —UIZMUI H. RJVK

69. XN'A H KTITAAXDU LVTU SDOK
UTXWVGDK YDATA VXA RDG; XN'A H
FTBKTAAXDU LVTU SDO YDAT SDOKA.

                    -VHKKS A. NKOEHU

70. EHP'A GYYM B FBP WTYOORPW AHH
CHPW - LY'O OTQY AH NRPE ALY
BPOZYQ OHFYZLYQY YCOY.

                         -FBY ZYOA

71. GQCFC TQHADM RC X YQKDMFCJ'T
THJO: "KP SHA'FC QXZZS XJM SHA
VJHL KG, VCCZ KG GH SHAFTCDP XJM
DCG SHAF MXM TDCCZ."

                         -UKE OXPPKOXJ

72. WY W ZRHV VE AHEJA R NVEUX EYY
VMB YUEHV KRDB, W QSNV JMRHDB IX
MRWUNVXOB.

—MWOORUX JOWHVEH

73. WMGWEM HFG JFRBU JFMP UBGH
MLMDPJFRBQ SDM S QDMSJ SBBGPSBZM
JG JFGYM GT AY HFG VG.

—RYSSZ SYROGL

74. L DEPROB HA V XPDCVMA DCVTX.
CEVC'D CEA PYOZ KVZ L'OO ANAW MAC
OLQFAB.

—TREVTTVB VOL

75. ZQ PKXS ZDGQ DUF K IDOS CSSU
ZDGGKSF XJG XJGBQ-NSOSU QSDGN DUF
UJB JUHS IDOS PS IDF DU DGYVZSUB
NSGKJVN SUJVYI BJ HJUNKFSG

FKOJGHS; ZVGFSG, QSN, CVB FKOJGHS,
USOSG.

-TDHL CSUUQ

76. HFMUWRY GBDR UWR GBE. EBDRI
JRMJFR WBLR FXUUFR MN EM XEPFSREHR
XE YMHXRUA.

-GBND UZBXE

77. WFB DBQSBW GC DWXNVUK NGPUK VD
WG JVOB FGUBDWJN, BXW DJGYJN, XUT
JVB XIGPW NGPS XKB.

-JPQVJJB IXJJ

78. GMJHPHNQ HQ RMP O EOU
GCMAFQQHMR. HA ZMS QSNNFFU PKFCF
OCF VORZ CFXOCUQ, HA ZMS UHQDCONF

ZMSCQFJA ZMS NOR OJXOZQ XCHPF O

EMMY.   —CMROJU CFODOR

79. LXXAYIEBU QA L BPG RVYZPC, 90%

AO TPB RLC QSPEY MAZPY ER LMRA

QSPEY DPRQ OYEPBI. GSEXS ER YPLMMC

NEBI AO IERQVYDEBU GSPB CAV

XABREIPY TLB'R DPRQ OYEPBI ER SER

IAU.   —FLC MPBA

80. RO ZXS MXWJ UX B OXPE RD UGJ

PXBC, UBEJ RU.

                            —ZXQR KJPPB

81. DWVW'C TK WTCO ETO HP NXMLVW

PLH XN OPL'VW XK T QLRH: XN OPL'VW

EPKSWVXKM EDWHDWV OPL'VW XK T
QLRH, HDW TKCEWV XC OWC.

-CHWFDWK QPRYWVH

82. VMRH VHMMJM QZ VJ ACGH RS JWH
IJMWQWL CWE EQZPJBHM VFCV UJRM
FQLF ZPFJJN PNCZZ QZ MRWWQWL VFH
PJRWVMU.

-GRMV BJWWHLRV

83. N VYDDRVVHYG JNF PV AFR TWA
JNXRV JAZR JAFRU CWNF WPV TPHR DNF
VBRFE. N VYDDRVVHYG TAJNF PV AFR
TWA DNF HPFE VYDW N JNF.

-GNFN CYZFRZ

84. K OEUOZW UOVPJA PT IJ
WTNJITAZ, IFP VTU K DJOEKBJ K
WSTFEA SOGJ IJJV NTDJ WQJRKXKR.

-EKEZ PTNEKV

85. NC FBKVNYNBA EWB KF NMBW BDNF
GXFF, BDXM PDA OSM'B NB EXB KF
WKB?

-PNTT QWEXQF

86. VZ SMYEKZ BH SMJS JPP EC
HOESSBHM OWBHBQY BH TJHYX EQ J
XJKY.

-VBDY VZYKH

87. B'G UYBWBJL K IQQA. B'CR LQW
WDR VKLR JSGIRYE FQJR.

                    -EWRCRJ UYBLDW

88. JIX EPVA JKWX M ZEWMP YXMVVA
QLGGXXUQ KP GIMPRKPR M WMP KQ ZIXP
IX KQ M HMHA.

                    -PMJMVKX ZEEU

89. EPZP'N XHH VAW EXKP CA GLAF
XDAWC UPL XLY FAUPL: FAUPL XZP
SZXBV, UPL XZP NCWJTY. XLY CEP
UXTL ZPXNAL FAUPL XZP SZXBV TN
CEXC UPL XZP NCWJTY.

                    -RPAZRP SXZHTL

90. OCGQ KMNOQ PMHHDBQOO SPQIQLQI
RPQV FC; CRPQIO SPQBQLQI RPQV FC.

-COKMI SDTYQ

91. O QGULB HX L IUSSUG SHBHGGHV,
VMUGU DMODTUPR DLP DGHRR SMU GHLQ
LPQ PHS IU ENURSOHPUQ LIHNS SMUOG
BHSOKUR.

-GLJAM VLJQH UBUGRHP

92. CJQ GND'A AJSQ FUXS YK AJUDFK
CS ZMD MZAYMHHQ YKS? U GND'A DSSG
M AJUDDSO RJNDS. QNY EDNC CJMA U
DSSG? U DSSG M ANOAUHHM ZJUR AJMA

38

ZMD KYRRNOA AJS CSUFJA NL
FYMZMTNHS.

-SHHSD GSFSDSOSK

93. ARV DPK RKEA QN ARVKO RKDN.
QVJ ARV DPK PEIPAL QN GYYPJVUN.

-BPSN QPUUA

94. XBGKZX FWZJ GLB QISFQ ZI PBBK
JZWUSE JIVBEGN, KNSFQ SF XIJUSZGKJ
ENSFQ IP FIZXSFQ.

-LBEE PIAA

95. HZ DGYTQAF JVQKXJLBBZ CQFXK
XGLYR V NVZ ZGL PVZ CECAKLVBBZ FCK

KG HC HGRR VAN DGYT KDCBEC XGLYR V
NVZ.

-YGHCYK JYGRK

96. KS MEH DJIX XE AJUF VEL BJHVR,
XFBB RKA JWEHX MEHT CBJIP.

-DEELM JBBFI

97. C XRJ R NMIJSKDTG QXCGJXMMJ,
NXCQX CB HMTYX FSQRTBS CH'B XRKJ
HM RJLTBH HM R WCBSKRFGS
RJTGHXMMJ.

-GRKKU JRACJ

98. GWN WVKYQ DIYOQ OR RTNLOYJ. OG
RGYIGR UHIPOQS YR RHHQ YR CHV SNG
VT YQA OG AHNRQ'G RGHT VQGOJ CHV
SNG GH RLWHHJ.

                              —KOJGHQ DNIJN

99. XCRD OGV'UR QD IGZR QE'F ECR
HGFE MIGUQGVF EXG JDT J CJIW TJOF
GW OGVU IQWR.

                              —UQYCJUT IRXQF

100. V LYGVYXY BOEB VI GVIY TVXYU
WNA GYKNMU, WNA UONAGF KECY
GYKNMEFY… EMF BDW BN IVMF UNKYLNFW
QONUY GVIY OEU TVXYM BOYK XNFCE,
EMF OEXY E JEDBW.

101. Q OQVM BGPGLQEQRV LGDA
GMKUNBQVT. GLGDA BQWG ERWGHRMA
BKDVE RV BSG EGB, Q TR QVBR BSG
RBSGD DRRW NVM DGNM N HRRC.

—TDRKUSR WNDJ

102. L HPG'F FCLGV BGDPGX MCPTWH
INLFX FCXLN BTFPKLPSNBQCD TGFLW
BOFXN FCXD'NX HXBH.

—MBJTXW SPWHIDG

103. RIUXNGM IEVPR CPBNK NB UNXD
SIGKNGM IEVPR IOKQNRDKRPOD.

—BRDJD CIORNG

104. PQCQGP BGR, SRG OHRM, LP
DCQLH VRK "QTX NXPP MX'KX LH".

                        -KRHCDW KXCJCH

105. Q TGEA P IPG AUE WPLX CR
DIETQGW, VOQGTQGW, DXK, PGV OQSU
NEEV. UX APD UXPBMUZ OQWUM CR ME
MUX VPZ UX TQBBXV UQIDXBN.

                        -HEUGGZ SPODEG

106. PSTPTFQEBJ MSB BMJG. CDBG CSG
CT NQEE MKF BMC GTW. LBTLEB MSB
DMSFBS. JTOBCQOBJ CDBG LSBCBKF CT
IB GTWS VSQBKF VQSJC.

                        -JCBHB QSXQK

107. CXGXN DM OM FXS EBS. VOBZ PH
BCS QTDIO.

                    —HIZWWTV STWWXN

108. HBEBL UQXI W SQATO JQOT WH
RADC UBLZPH, OTBC'EB APO HPOTQHA
OP DPZB.

                    —LPGQH JQDDQWFZ

109. FXPCPVH APYC LXW JT X
ROXVAMTCC DIJ ZPRO FPYPKGMIGC
OIGFC, JGR XR MTXCR ROT EXW CGKAC.

                    —DPL HXQQPHXV

44

110. URCBC'K YI KMVR URSYO FK KIX
LSJP. SU'K KIX NMSVC.

-JCTSK QJFVP

111. QW BIN DINCS AQDA GTV XVORIF
QF GTV XHFGR OVRXIFRQPCV WIO YIRG
IW BINO GOINPCV, BIN ZINCSF'G RQG
WIO H YIFGT.

-GTVISIOV OIIRVJVCG

112. ANLNS PM DM G VMBDMS HEMUN
MIICBN FKGADU EGLN VCNV.

-NSWG RMWRNBO

113. H EGGV IYFFST ITGNCV WF CZJF
H AGLHD'I IJZMU: CGDE FDGNET UG

SGBFM UTF INWKFSU HDV ITGMU FDGNET
UG SMFHUF ZDUFMFIU.

                    -AZDIUGD STNMSTZCC

114. WQP OSGJB WSBHI BSPNE'W XHZP
NPENP, NS OQI NQSDJB F RHFEW
RFMWDGPN WQHW BS?

                        -RHTJS RFMHNNS

115. TCB TG VMB ZYBPV VMFCZJ PRTIV
RTTUJ FJ JTNBVFNBJ VMBYB PYB JTNB
GPCVPJVFQ LFQVIYBJ.

                        -ZBTYZB K. RIJM

116. IBW JWOI REN IF IWEUB NFQC
XLZO EJFQI IEVWO LO JN WEILAT 30
DWCUWAI FK IBWLC LUW UCWEH.

                         —JLSS HQCCEN

117. FA OTIOOF EQ IBET YPWQIGA BMT
KPQO WN TWVTIMQIEMZZA. EI ET LOGA
QEYO QPS IBMI SBOQ NOPNZO SMLO MI
FO, IBOA WTO MZZ IBOEG XEQKOGT.

                         —DEFFA YMGIOG

118. OJB'YD AJK KJ ID YDPO HEPDLBR
ZL OJB SJT'K GTJF FQDPD OJB EPD
AJZTA, IDHEBMD OJB WZAQK TJK ADK
KQDPD.

                         —OJAZ IDPPE

47

119. WSJOSW, KBEELKS QLB TSWS JR FOFLD. JRO KBEELKS QLB TSWS J ISIASW LY HLRPWSKK. ABD F WSESJD IQKSNY.

-IJWC DTJFR

120. XGWR GI JDGJXD FVEW WG UQZD FQWC HGP QE WCD XQKG, NPW FCVW HGP FVEW QR RGKDGED FCG FQXX WVSD WCD NPR FQWC HGP FCDE WCD XQKG NUDVSR ZGFE.

-GJUVC FQEIUDH

121. N RYBX EA DVAJCNORMNVR RCOR ZTZMAYGZ CORZV EZ. CZ VONX N UOV

HZNGS MNXNJWBYWV - ZTZMAYGZ COVG'R
EZR EZ AZR.

                    -MYXGZA XOGSZMPNZBX

122. OZ WYDE WKVEI GFJEVFP JFA KD
BHDE EF PYNCY EIY PKLIED FJ.

                         -BFNJ VKCYVD

123. OW'F IRIUOJB WAIW WAX IRHQJW
HS JXPF WAIW AIZZXJF OJ WAX PHVME
XKXVG EIG IMPIGF DQFW XLINWMG SOWF
WAX JXPFZIZXV.

                    -DXVVG FXOJSXME

124. FBMYZ, ABNNKSRO ADONKMOIFKYR
EYIMKMYFO MBIYRM FDHJA DOROYNOM
QKN SKDFQ EODFKLKEYFO. KF RKNFN
QKN OZON YN SRHO YIM QKN QYKD YN
DKMKEHRBHN.

                    -EBIYI B'SDKOI

125. GNT, WNC IL LNMGXOC ZVOTOCH
NMA AFOCO, K UNNR VH HNIOAFVGX TO
MHOS AN FKZO UOWNCO AFO VGAOCGOA.
VA'H HNCA NW K UBNX WNC JONJBO
TVAF KAAOGAVNG HJKGH.

                    -HAOJFOG QNBUOCA

126. MO AIH'XZ KIMYK JI RI
LINZJBMYK JIYMKBJ JBGJ AIH'VV EZ
LIXXA OIX JINIXXIS NIXYMYK, LVZZT
VGJZ.

                    —BZYYA AIHYKNGY

127. UNN EQOTM FSFEABPF, NQPF DR
UNRTUWFMQZUNNA UZZBEXQPO MB ABDE
TFQOTM.

                    —ZUJFA JMFPOFN

128. O XVFOVKV NBVPV OR RCDVNBOAJ
CQN NBVPV TZNEBOAJ QR.
QAYCPNQAZNVFG, ON'R NBV
JCKVPADVAN.

                    —TCCLG ZFFVA

129. MNFRQ AS NAZ EMLYFG MNK
HTKBHVK YKBEAR FE, HRG BKHXFCK
NHXS AS MNKO HBK EMLYFGKB MNHR
MNHM.

                        —VKABVK WHBXFR

130. VGBCINQKCG CZ G ICKS EBGVS PN
BCOS — CI HNR YGEESK PN XS GK
NQGKLS.

                        —IQSW GBBSK

131. RAB JFMR QGBXXBLRQOB TFWNBWM
CWB MDMRBJCRQLCVVD JFOBU RF RAB
KVCLB TABWB RABD LCG UF RAB VBCMR
UCJCPB: JCGCPBJBGR.

                        —MLFRR CUCJM

52

132. NW CXNE NE VGWWKK, IOKPEK
FDNSY TK EGTK CKP; FLC NW CXNE NE
CKP, IOKPEK FDNSY TK EGTK VGWWKK.

                    -PFDPXPT ONSVGOS

133. NZW RMZD NZW'JH XHQQCMX ZSI
DTHM NZW PQZZG QZ QCH NZWJ
PTZHSOUHP OMI DZMIHJ DTOQ HSPH NZW
UZWSI IZ DTCSH NZW'JH IZDM QTHJH.

                    -XHZJXH VWJMP

134. HP'M PJZA TFJU LYJC XAKAJ
CHEEAU FXOVYUO, VZP H IHWZJA, LTO
PFCA PTA RTFXRA?

—JYXFEU JAFWFX

135. DN WZVN CGGZMMHY NC TH NLEN
NLH TEWCMDNB CJ TB YDHN DV TEYH ZI
CJ NLH JCCYV NLEN TB RDY YDYO'N
JDODVL.

—GEMMDH ZOYHMACCY

136. MLQUQRQA YXHQXUQ FSJJY HQ
NDJE O DQP YNGQA YSK SUK LND PLQH,
CQFSNYQ O VUXM LXM PXNDL JOIQ OY
IXA PLQ ROYNSJJE OHGSOAQK.

—MOJJ IQAAQJJ

137. R EKGF FI P DKNFPXDPGF FOPF
NKDHKN "LDKPUCPNF PF PGQ FRVK". NI

R IDSKDKS CDKGMO FIPNF SXDRGW FOK
DKGPRNNPGMK.

-NFKHKG EDRWOF

138. T HENQ SW IN ERWY YATSN, IHS
T QDTKSNQ.

-JFN YNES

139. XAJD NMHE YAWVUEJD LEJ
GJJDLIJEB, WG'B WFTMEGLDG GM ALRJ
L UMI BM GALG BMFJMDJ WD GAJ AMHBJ
WB ALTTN GM BJJ NMH.

-DMEL JTAEMD

140. BZBMDKECIQ CU WERIQCIQ.
YBHYSB RMB KROCIQ KEB WHXBVCRIU

UBMCHGUSD RIV KEB YHSCKCWCRIU RU R
LHOB.

-NCSS MHQBMU

141. KRLMKEHXB, MT M ISH HNDMKEH
SRKEU GSLMVA S DNXSUMKVHGMO IMUG
HKCNKVN XKVA-UNDC, UGN XSHU ONKOXN
M IKEXY MVUDKYEFN GMC UK IKEXY RN
CB TSCMXB.

-FGNXHNS GSVYXND

142. MX DTSC KNG WNES VSGMKMHHMG
RBD RX WRHFC UQSNF, DTSC KNG OBQS
WNES ORWSDTMGY RBD RX CRB.

-WBTNWWNF NHM

143. JW 4 WKIA FZT QFH PILK JK I
XIHT JITK YIAT CFA CINXKA'Q TIW.
JIWUK CFA YXAOQNJIQ O'ZZ TAIR XOJ
I EOYNSAK FC QFJK NFWQ.

　　　　　　　　　　　　—DOJ PICCOPIH

144. RYL USKKLQLZOL JLRXLLZ
ARNESUSRC PZU ILZSNA SA RYPR
ILZSNA YPA SRA HSGSRA.

　　　　　　　　　　　　—PHJLQR LSZARLSZ

145. TX EGPBKRG QH OMX MDC TX
JMGRDBH CPD'B NMGR, MH IPDO MH KR
TMGGQRH M CPNBPG.

　　　　　　　　　　　　—RIMXDR EPPHIRG

57

146. CEVXMD BCHGCQM PT KFHHECO KCQ GXCFM EQ FKCHEGF. MXC HCJM GXCFM EQ CZHPBC.   —LFGUEC KFJPQ

147. POSE LXT'CS WE FIWM, I VXXB QCWSEB PWMM RS KCLWEV KX RIWM LXT XTK. I RSAK QCWSEB PWMM RS WE KOS NSMM ESJK KX LXT AILWEV, "BIGE, KOIK PIA QTE".

                              —VCXTNOX GICJ

148. V UXJR MATJ X ARXY ETSZK QRVZKCTAKTTL. TQUR X ZSH OSYYRL X PQVMR TQ JR. V PQRB KR BXIQ'E X OATMRIIVTQXY, EKR PQVMR KXL CSEERA TQ VE.

149. U WJAIR ZKR XKF W NUAI, NYD U
AVKM ZKR RKIJV'D MKFA DEWD MWS. JK
U JDKQI W NUAI WVR WJAIR XKF
XKFZUOIVIJJ.

150. NDZNLW XGJJGZ IGAHL BJGI N
YHWWVIVWP. MH ZGA'P HSYHKP VP
XNKE.

151. UP UA Q AMUWLPUKUM KQMP PBQP
TXNE FXRT YUJJ LXP QFAXEF
MBXJWAPWEXJ UK TXN PQCW UP KEXI
QLXPBWE SWEAXL'A SJQPW.

152. LX YERZS RC, JRNA RC MPEVS PMJMZQA. SOA DEEI MZI SOA PMI. SOA ORDOC MZI SOA JEKC. SOA YRZM MZI SOA QEJMIM.

—AJJAZ IADAZAFAC

153. LQGWLEEA H ILES LDVWUB IHGN GNO OFFA INODOPOD H RV, JWG H'F PODA QLKWLE LJVWG HG.

—ELDDA BLPHB

154. RYQJQ WJQ VLKA RYJQQ RYPLSD OVTQL LQQC PL KPZQ: ZVVC, OWRQJ WLC NVTBKPTQLRD.

—NYJPD JVNI

155. F'D XVA GPTGFC VP CSGAM; F
HKEA CVX'A NGXA AV OS AMSTS NMSX
FA MGWWSXE.

—NVVCQ GIISX

156. IUH RNV UFQXZYX N AUE FI KHQE
GNERCOVT.

—IUTO FXZZN

157. AQVH YOH KISV TY EIXV
TEBIXAOMA AQOM EIMVH… QOSV HIN
AXTVG BOHTMC HINX PTKKY JTAQ O
QNC?

—GOSV UQOBBVKKV

158. W MDXA NT AWJS GWY QDZJSXDG.
JSPJ'G SZA W OXPDIXE JZ EPIHX:
APWJWIM RZD JSX QPJSDZZK.

-QZQ SZTX

159. HPJ OEGTCJK ABHP CBWJ BM, TS
HPJ HBKJ SGX NLD EJLY AGKJD CBQJ L
TGGQ, SGXE CBTELES NLEY PLM
JZOBEJY.

-KBCHGD TJECJ

160. WYVZD OAR, YAJQKJVMBQY, TAJ
CKBZE ZKBWYKJ V JVMBQY ZAJ V
YAJQK. UYVW OAR VJK BQ V SBVJ
TAAM.

62

—PBFFO TVSSAZ

161. FUBT Q JBQKUBC KQZZO Q MNW MW
USO BTJSCB TQLB, SJ LBQTO JCNVMZB.

—LQCD JFQST

162. A JPET GPRT FH GD GAKR CJPC A
GFVC JPET GYKTD, HP. A BTTW CJPC A
SPK'C UTZ AC, UYQQYX AC, YQ VCTPW
AC; PKR VY A JPET QTVYWETR CJPC A
GFVC GPQQD AC.

—SJPQWTV RASMTKV

163. MW ICSOMTI QSIGK I RQSKKSG
QMWS, DJSP NJX GMG ZFG ULD IQQ FW
FLO FMQ LPGSO USFUQS NJF JIDS LK?

164. DK BQNBO DR GYHNBJ, OEX IEFY
SE ESY OHR BOYDQ OHDQ TESY DS BOY
ADGQHQJ?

—ADAJ BEFADS

165. L BLMA W OQFWH OLGT W TAWV QH
TAK RTQDBVAKR. L TWGA HASMR.

—RGACA FWKGLH

166. C MIWB HMBR RBH GIYBRWO IOF
HMK WMB QIQV PKKFO PCFB! CW HIO
QKYR 15 TCRZWBO ILK, CW PKKFO PCFB
I GKWIWK.

167. XWFWFPWX, GYWK DZI UXW BWUB,
DZI BZ KZS LKZG DZI UXW BWUB. JS
JH ZKVD QUJKEIV EZX ZSYWXH. SYW
HUFW UQQVJWH GYWK DZI UXW HSIQJB.

    -XJOLD AWXMUJH

168. MAPL ZJH'QP XJQL ZJH UPY I
YVSDPY YJ YAP KQPID WAJM. MAPL
ZJH'QP XJQL VL IFPQVSI, ZJH UPY I
KQJLY QJM WPIY.   -UPJQUP SIQEVL

169. BW YFJ WYFEHBEP WRLXSJD
IRELSH FD LY GRJS RTYFL LXS JSDL
YW LXS IYJMH, LXSQ IYFMHE'L XRAS

HSGMRJSH LXSBJ BEHSKSEHSEGS WJYV
BL.

                    —DLSKXSE GYMTSJL
170. RCGGWQDDE YK XRD UDIYEEYEI WT
XRD RWGYSCM KRWFFYEI KDCKWE.
XRCX'K TWO QWVDE. XRD UDIYEEYEI WT
XRD RWGYSCM KRWFFYEI KDCKWE TWO
VDE YK JROYKXVCK DND.

                         —SCNYS GDXXDOVCE

171. ADZN NH QRMZDFVPZQ GDYPWMD KF
QPWSBNDJ'M HGMDMMDQ ARNB KRYLDF
KHWMD. MBD APM MH DTYRNDQ ABDZ R
SHN BHKD PZQ NHVQ BDJ.

                         —JFPZ JDFZHVQM

172. OTK PKFZKO UI VSIK SP TUXKPOE

HXN IHSZ NKHVSXQ. SI EUG FHX IHJK

OTHO, EUG'MK QUO SO BHNK.

                          -QZUGFTU BHZA

173. V XYQVL XUWRXHQWXQ HR NRNVYYP

AIQ RHKW UM V CVJ OQOULP.

                          -RAQSQW ELHKIA

174. L GO HDI G OBOUBN DR GHV

DNEGHLXBA SDFLILJGF SGNIV. L GO G

ABODJNGI.

                          -ZLFF NDEBNQ

175. K VXXLZW RN PA MEPKVA DGZZ
ECW MXRCW XRD K BEI DFZ IEN.

                    —GXWCZA WECHZGMKZVW

176. DMKEZN VKKXLOR EYNLQLZNZ HAEO
NJ XKZYKOX JO IEZGLORNJO VJM E
HFDALY DMKEZN VKKXLOR
XKPJOZNMENLJO. EAZJ XKZYKOXLOR JO
IEZGLORNJO, NGJFZEOXZ JV PKO
ZESLOR, "IGEN? L'P AJJULOR EN NGK
DEDS".

                    —YJOEO J'DMLKO

68

177. ENLLK N ENG KCBL CPG NIU; NX KCBL YUNBFK VNTUX, XC PWSS OWX UKUXWIOF.

                            -AOKSSWX TWSSUL

178. EL VTK QJJU KTEF LVTL HXBELEOK EK LVJ KJOXUF XBFJKL HSXNJKKEXU. E VTPJ BJTSUJF LVTL EL QJTSK T KLSEGEUM SJKJAQBTUOJ LX LVJ NESKL.

                            -SXUTBF SJTMTU

179. QV XLF RYSB XLFW TDQUKWOS BL UQHBOS, BWX BYUEQSZ HLVBUX BL HLGOLSO OUHO.

                            -YSS UYSKOWH

69

180. TB LOY RYIRQY XIC'L GUCL LI

MISY IJL LI LOY VUQQRUAN, CIVIXD'H

KITCK LI HLIR LOYS.

                              -DIKT VYAAU

181. LUZA MR Z PZAV, SVZBBW, OTA Z

XKO MYAVSNMVL AUZA BZRAR ZBB

YMQUA? AUV KYBW PMCCVSVYEV MR AUZA

MY YKA DZYW XKO MYAVSNMVLR MR

AUVSV Z EUZYEV WKT'BB LMYP TF

YZGVP.

                              -XVSSW RVMYCVBP

70

182. N INIZ'X CYNT XOG XGRX. N
SQRX CEQZI 100 JYAR XE IE NX
JBEZP.

                        -VGZSYFNZ CBYZHTNZ

183. SRPKHBYPSY HG OFLA ZRN FLQY
UYKRWY ZRN NPBYWGALPB AFY MWRUTYE.
                        -ORRBZ LTTYP

184. QP ADX WVQYI ADX SOU WDD
JFSKK WD FSIU S TQPPUOUYMU, WOA
JKUUHQYE ZQWV S FDJCXQWD.
                        -TSKSQ KSFS

185. CFF TM EV RCQZ STSZBOV WB TEL
FWQZV ORCO OZVO TEL DTELCXZ.

OCIWBX DRWFKLZB WBOT C RTEVZ YWOR

C YRWOZ DCLGZO WV TBZ TM ORZS.

                    —ZLSC ATSAZDI

186. RMEUQDERDR QSI OUBEUNU DLTD

DLU VXEGTXP OESBSYEMTB WZQMDESQ SW

OXUTRDR ER DS GTJU GUQ RDZVEH.

                    —HTNU OTXXP

187. EM TWQGJ ULJ RDG TWUCH TG

TWACHJ'R DLKG TLUI, XAIR EJRGJIG

JGBWRELREWJI GKGUF 28 HLFI.

                    —UWVEJ TECCELQI

188. NK MYQ RCG HYS MGUUNHL RS
MYQC VNEI, MYQ RCG HYS IWGHENHL
GHYQLB SNZG ANSB SBGZ.

                    —CGGIG ANSBGCIWYYH

189. YB JCIRTRHRPT PI XT
RTHCUUCOHVXU RG GPYCPTC ZDP OXT
URGHCT HP HDC ZRUURXY HCUU
PMCSHVSC ZRHDPVH HDRTNRTF PI HDC
UPTC SXTFCS.

                        —QRUUB OPTTPUUB

190. WXU SEB'P SAIWUPU MXPK SECU.
WVP SEBNHUG XB E SECU, XP'G E
FXZPKNED SECU. WVP SEBNHUG XB E

73

WXU, EBN GAIUFAND'G NZVBC XB PKU

CXPSKUB.

-RXI QELLXQEB

191. LXB QIXV JKOZO'R N UZXHDOP
VKOI LXB ZONDGYO JKNJ XBJ XE JKO
JKZOO ZR, XIDL XIO HOCGIR VGJK NI
Z.

-MOIIGR PGDDOZ

192. ZNLYIW SI BEIZQ YQ SIV SG ZPV
JSQZ PXJYOYEZYIW ZPYIWQ E JEI FEI

QXGGVN ZPEZ RSVQI'Z YICSOCV E
TSJEI.

                              —OENNL RECYR

193. GKTSU TDAAF TSU PKBWUH ZPSF
GWNN VPDUHS. TSU TDAAF GKTSU
PKBWUH ZPSF GWNN UKZ. QK SDVP WQ
WUSOWZDXNF CWQDBBKWUZSC.

                              —DNXSAZ SWUQZSWU

194. Q RLNY IDGQZYS GRLG YNYI
WYDWMY ERD ZMLQT YNYPUGRQIK QA

WPY-SYGYPTQIYS LIS GRLG EY ZLI SD
IDGRQIK GD ZRLIKY QG MDDC OYVDPY
GRYU ZPDAA GRY PDLS.

                    -AGYWRYI RLECQIK

195. WMB GAKZ YBGYKB XMG CWOKK
PTKK MNJJOPTABC TPWC GH IGR TJB
WMB YBGYKB XMG XJOWB OACNJTAPB
HGJEC.

                    -ABOK RBIJTCCB WZCGA

196. RC DZFLSK IT CTX LW HKI
RDBBLKZ: LM CTX MLJZ D HTTZ GLMK

CTX'VV AK QDOOC; LM JTI, CTX'VV
AKSTRK D OQLVTWTOQKB.

                        —WTSBDIKW

197. PH MBL FSQOCL GU OB YCQL BWCZ
IC'L NGO LPSXBQLU BQ OIC HVBBZ.

                        —EBSQ ZPWCZU

198. JALCIRW PU TICCJAT GRZZJIW
RTRJA, J'G TPJAT CP UJAW R XPGRA J
WPA'C HJYI RAW QMLC TJFI VIZ R
VPMLI.

                        —ZPW LCIXRZC

199. HRA GLDZ EWBAU EKZUA, ATRX GLD BWX PKUALZA ATRF WU GLD SIRWUR.

-FWZC AJWKX

200. QXVHMWWJ YF NYJH KXYN, OWP FYL XGWPIU XIU BXFLH LYCH, OWP BGYLH WI BXNNF XIU OWP THL SWJHU MO SHWSNH OWP UWI'L JIWB.

-BYNN QHGGHNN

201. ALVAQL HQMHZI HIC RL, "MLFL ZVO JOBBZ HI H DTNQX?" MLQQ, BV, N MHI HB HDDVOBGHBG.

-LQQLB XLULBLFLI

202. Q YGC JAQTJ IA CWD MAX

VDMGFGIQAT AM ZLGXGZIDX, EWI ILDT

Q XDGKQHDV Q LGRD TA ZLGXGZIDX.

                    -ZLGXKDC EGXPKDO

203. MYUS U HBN B XRS, B SRAN YBL

UCRIS SYK CBONT UEN SYK CKKT UEN

YK SRAN LK UCRIS SYK CISJYKO UEN

LW MBQK.

                    -ORNEKW NUEXKOQBKAN

204. LE'Y SAYE R SJI. VBRYY VBJFY,

ILBCY KXD, FRUMY OJATC EGM YRTC. L

IMRE OMJOXM AO.

                    -QAGRQQRC RXL

205. L BYAP XSVEPMPE YR RLOPG XBYR
RBP RPV JSOOYVEOPVRG XSKQE BYAP
QSSFPE QLFP LH OSGPG BYE MKV RBPO
RBMSKCB RBP KG JSVCMPGG.

                        —MSVYQE MPYCYV

206. M XMY JY BKCZ JP BJHZ M
SBJGGZQ SKNGKY — JD'P DJXZ DK SMPU
JY.

                        —XMZ LZPD

207. BKQYWSWL YK NISY ZOKZDO ASL
MSL, YIOWO'M QK PZZOW DXAXY KQ
MYPZXCXYL.

                        —MYOZIOQ BKDHOWY

80

208. VGT VDSHFUT PZVG OSBT PSBTL
ZO VGXV VGTW JTV XUU TMNZVTC XFSHV
LSVGZLJ, XLC VGTL VGTW BXDDW GZB.

                              —NGTD

209. APCK E CLCKBJMXXO VCB VD.
DEUPB E PMN KR ENCM BPMB PEG IEDGB
KMVC AMG MXAMOG.

                         —DEBM DJNKCD

210. ORW FTPPWIWMLW UWOSWWM
PTLOTAM JMF IWJKTOQ? PTLOTAM RJG
OA ZJEW GWMGW.

                         —OAZ LKJMLQ

211. KMTM'H HQNMRKZGY RQ RKZGS
CXQJR: KQB PQNM WQJ GMEMT HMM C
KMCOVZGM VZSM "FHWPKZP BZGH
VQRRMTW"?

                              -ICW VMGQ

212. RYS'O AGNVO OXN FNOOC OXJSKA
VSR RYS'O FNO OXN AGNVOC OXJSKA.

                         -KNYQKN UVQDJS

213. N'B OWU WCCHOVHV RM REWOVH
QWGHK RHLDSKH N GOWZ N'B OWU VSBR
... DOV N DEKW GOWZ UYDU N'B OWU
REWOVH.

                         -VWEEM IDJUWO

82

214. N RQ BZRIHJTA JKG ARTFZBMG,
MSPMWB YZMI QNAH PKQMX KTB KJ QV
IKXM.

-YKKCV RAAMI

215. ODDT OFSHL OD RD PNYANB, EYT
OFSHL OD NANSVMPNSN.

-PNHNB OCSHNV ESDMB

216. NH NWQ FY HFHSBHQ, JVU BQ
BFUHFQHAD MBQABLHM JD NBQ GEBHFMQ.

-YQRWE TBAMH

217. BYI BDELXSI HOBY BYOC ZELKBDQ
OC BYJB BYIDI JDI BEE UJKQ GIEGSI
VEOKV JXELB CJQOKV, "BYI BDELXSI
HOBY BYOC ZELKBDQ OC …"

                              —COKZSJOD SIHOC

218. U HLJX PTULE NCYVQYZLK HL AMH
HNNYDUHLD, MCKL U YV UL JHRK YLP
MCKL U YV LHA.

                              —NHNH NCYLKJ

219. GWTCJHYUH AR JAGH XWYHDCHND.
AZ AR XRHEXJ ZT LNMH AZ, PXZ WTZ
WHSHRRNDB ZT RLTC AZ TEE.

                              —PAJJ FXDDNB

220. FHWRFHEE MW 90% XRYAHE HYL
ABR JABRQ BHED MW KBGWMUHE.

                              —GJCM FRQQH

221. ANP XRU VTRZ R IRU GN
XNUEWTCC, SPG ANP XRU'G IRMT JFI
GJFUM.

                              —IFVGNU STWVT

222. RVFMS JBS GU NBZAHZNESM, JAK
ZO UFW KFA'R EZQS RVSG… CSEE Z
VJIS FRVSBM.

                              —LBFWHVF GJBP

223 QRD EBPC LKRLVK QKNK QBJK
WKVKIKPKWOF LRDKNG? NBOGK EC QBPU.

—KER LQOVOLG

224. F ZHK HW UTHUZT FDT FWDFOM HW
GTOIGKC. YHK JT, O'J FWDFOM HW
XOMKGC.

—CKTQTY XDOIGK

225. ECP LKECDHFL LCXULC CKM
KYYUDOPT K SPV KYY ECKE HPEM ZDX
NKWP LDSQPMMFDSM DOPU ZDXU FYCDSP.
FE KHMD UKFMPM ECP YDMMFJFHFEZ DQ
KLLFTPSEKHHZ JXEE-TFKHFSB BDT.

—LDSKS D'JUFPS

226. WVQCQ OA WVQ LQUQWICOIP VEW
MEGRQW YEC WVEAQ EY KA TVE NEP'W

TIPW WE QIW DQIW, XKW TEKJN AWOJJ
JORQ NOICCVQI.

                    -BOD UIYYOUIP

227. PQX WXHP RXIHZJX TD I RIG'H
QTGXHPC VHG'P QVH VGBTRX PIM
JXPZJG. VP'H PQX KXJT IANZHP TG
QVH WIPQJTTR HBIEX.

                    -IJPQZJ B. BEIJUX

228. G HZWZP ZABZJRZC RD IZZ ROZ
CXF NOZH SGPQI NDLQC SZR ILHTLPHZC
GH ROZ BQXJZI ROZF HDN CD.

                    -NGQQ PDSZPI

229. ZOQQJOEL JU O RHISLQMVF
JIUPJPVPJHI, NVP RGH RHVFS ROIP PH
FJDL JI OI JIUPJPVPJHI?

-G. F. ZLIBALI

230. AB RCXK ETCWLM QFKQ UKSCDMK F
QFQ WGL EJKLKWQ LG OCLKJ LIKA.

-AFLSI IKQUKJP

231. XBVVNEJFF NF XBYNEO B UBSOJ,
UIYNEO, LBSNEO, LUIFJ-HENK PBDNUR
NE BEIKXJS LNKR.

-OJISOJ TCSEF

88

232. NL FOTLYSV ONXSE TLOCARB
JLOVEJ NXXIP. ZXS QOZ CAL XY O
QAPGTARE.

                        -QOTI EDOAR

233. R BYPQJ'K DUVAQJ KV HI TRMQ
RJ IQYWD. R CRCJ'K TYJK KV
RJKQWWNUK BQW.

                    -WVCJQI CYJLQWMRQOC

234. XVSO UGOLI'M VTVMCMO CHM, VM
VTVMCMOL ECU MOXOJVLVGI.

                        -QGGUA CXXOI

89

235. KCE GRCI KCE'AB QBJJORQ CDW
ILBR KCE QBJ JLXJ CRB VXRWDB CR
JLB VXGB. OJ'P DOGB, "PBB OT KCE
VXR YDCI JLOP CEJ".

-SBAAK PBORTBDW

236. M JCG VGKD LMJXBMA MQIYTS KLG
BIQJS ZGXIQG KLG KQYKL LMD M
HLMTHG KI VGK CKD NMTKD IT.

-BCTDKIT HLYQHLCJJ

237. MU M CKW IR NMPG LH NMUG
RPGZ, M'W NMPG RPGZ K FKNRRE.

-O. A. UMGNWF

238. LPQWUX TKAAKEXQY QYNK XUSM,
"FK XPQRJM YKZKE TRMBK U IEKXSMKYL
HO PSX UBK, QYJO HO PSX FQEDX."
UYM KZKE XSYNK PK LQJM WK LPUL, S
XLQIIKM FQEEOSYB.

                    —EQYUJM EKUBUY

239. T BVY'P NTWG PV MG VEP VD AZ
HVADVLP CVYG, JFTHF TK RMVEP R
FRND RY TYHF JTBG.

                    —NRLLZ BRXTB

240. ZKI FIO HU VHCKZHIG ZKEO ZKI
UXPGR, HN APW UKPPZ ZKEZ FIO PWZ
PN E CWO.

                    —UZIFKIO QPTDIGZ

241. X CAZT DXJNTI DAYPT DAGT SWLF LFI OADLF X WLZT TZTG NFAOF.

                              -OLCS MXPFTI

242. MD M VYSY JVQ-DUOYB, VQGPB M RY VYUSMWN JIMT QWY?

                              -URSUIUX PMWOQPW

243. Y QME FJKFVHYZF HMYBH. BTFE RMHB UNNC ATFGK NV PF.

                              -LGWWFV QMXXFBB

244. GLZOQT GV UP DNIIZ UZ NRRWFWKNGOQT IVYYPYYOVQY OY KOHP GLZOQT GV YNGOYMZ DWQTPL UZ GNIOQT YNQJBORDPY NKK VEPL ZVWL UVJZ.

92

-TPVLTP RNLKOQ

245. S OCXF C BVARFKLTG DCNF-TJ
IKFB. UOFP'KF UOF HCDF JFVJGF
KFHUVKSAQ UOF HUCUTF VL GSMFKUP.

                        -MVM OVJF

246. F'T CMFUC WM TKQQD K XJBFRY
BMTKU AJVKSRJ F IFLJ WYJ FEJK MO
CJWWFUC SN RSUEKD TMQUFUC KUE
CMFUC WM WYJ EJIF.

                  -TFVYKJI X. OMZ

93

247. F TAE'G OAAP OFPQ BLOOQ
CQYYU. CNG ZBLEZQW LYQ, WBQ'W
XAFEX GA QET NV OAAPFEX OFPQ SQ.

                              -HBAAVF XAOTCQYX

248. XMACS SOV WNESNA SNGW IV SOV
QNNW RVJC: M JPC QNMRQ SN OPFV P
WMCVPCV RPIVW PXSVA IV.

                              -CSVFV IPASMR

249. LTSTN QLPTN XLM HFNHQKDGXLHTD
GXIT X DVTTUFLW UFVV XLP X
VXZXGFST RL GET DXKT LFWEG.

                              -PXST CXNNM

250. V NUQR DZ FYVBITCQ RS YUEC
UBB RYC RYVQMP V FSXBIQ'R UHHSTI.
RYCQ V NUQR RS DSEC VQ NVRY RYCD.

                        -GYZBBVP IVBBCT

251. QU CB UQEVB ZAF NAR'B
VFYYXXN... VA DFYL UAE VPZNQSQRJ.

                        -LXRRZ ZAFRJDCR

252. Q HNJP VPSVHQWPG. Q HQIP BCP
ECNNGCQWK GNLWV BCPA DSIP SG BCPA
RHA XA.   -VNLKHSG SVSDG

253. VY WZMB VI OQB NRIABP, HZLWK
SZL UWBNIB PBUQPNIB OQB GLBIOVZR?

                        -WVWS OZDWVR

254. XPD XTQDVA QDCD AT XPYOB XPDCD Y OTGVN PICNVZ OVTAD LZ AGYXOIAD.   -ZTKY EDCCI

255. ORH FKEA TOR IC FAOPZEZLG. OAA HZL UOXC SZ BZ KG GSORB GSKAA ORB AZZM GSLQKB.

       -UCBH AOPOEE

256. ZJV TLJO ZJV UVEQ IG RJFLN EJUGQDFLN CFNDQ FM JXR SGJSXG XFTG ZJV.

       -RYPG WDYSSGXXG

257. IVXPT MPJD LWV DQYLXGVY JM JLWVPY. RJK UXT TVAVP IQAV IJTO VTJKOW LJ DXGV LWVD XII RJKPYVIM.

-OPJKUWJ DXPS

258. AFQ ZJJ XQOP XFNJ FR AFQN
OPUVMNJH FHOJ IPJA VJCGJ PFXJ.

-VQOUVVJ DCVV

259. VJVO CABPVO CKXF EVAESV HAF
IVRQR YAO MKODRFUXR? DF'R SDNV,
"AK HOVXF, RAMNR. ZAQ NBAC D'U
PZDBH YAO ZAQO RDBR ODHKF? ZVXK,
LQF FKXBNR YAO FKV RAMNR! FKVZ'SS
HA HOVXF CDFK UZ RXBPXSR."

-IDU HXYYDHXB

97

260. M LHUX H DXA BLMOQWQBLP. M'G
QDOP KQMDK CQ IEXHI QDX IHP HC H
CMGX.

                        -JLHEOXW G. WJLZOF

261. F YOIE VS HSP TYV VMI FDI
DYTIO XIKV BURRFQP SYV SB CW
PRUOO.

                        -EUZFE RII NSVM

262. R'O IRBA SIH PRWA. GKAQ HSW'G
YJRWL OA SNG DAJQ SUGAW - YNG R'O
PAII VJAMAJDAH.

                        -JSMA BAWWAHQ

263. ONIB EZH QXI WZHXLJBS Q BJWI SJXT QB NZHX VIIRV TJCI Q VIWZBG. ONIB EZH VJL ZB Q XIG-NZL WJBGIX Q VIWZBG VIIRV TJCI QB NZHX. LNQL'V XITQLJDJLE.   —QTYIXL IJBVLIJB

264. NTM ZKKO ZI DZVED NZ NTM ONZLM IZL S FZSI ZI XLMSK SEK WZGVED ZRN YVNT ZEFH S FZSI ZI XLMSK SLM NTLMM XVFFVZE NZ ZEM.

                              —MLGS XZGXMWU

265. QEIYEZY TQFYR IY, VK V CYSY QBSTZRYR EZ T RYQYSB VQXTZR CMTB LEEF CEJXR V LSVZD… "MEC BE LJVXR T LETB."

—QBYAYZ CSVDMB

266. FX RBVQLFCIOWB JIVBIWL
ZVHYGQR EGTW FGHWJ V LVX ZOWQ JOW
ZVJ JGDIX. JOW'J QGQWIX-JWTWQ QCZ,
VQL ZW LCQ'I YQCZ ZOWBW IOW OWHH
JOW GJ.

—WHHWQ LWRWQWBWJ

267. PYSJWK YLYAV NAYUD ZUW JE U
MQZUW AQOOJWN SYA YVYE.

—GJZ RUAAYV

268. WTGL LGLUAQHA HN TM TR PLUL
AXFU WHNR ELKHFNL NXYLQHA AXF'UL
IXTVI RX EL UTIBR.

—YFBHYYHQ HWT

269. JNKQP JGWK SV OLA GKDP JNKQP
SK OLA LSVOGWP GT NBAWSJN OLNO'V
KAZAW FAAK NQZAWOSVAQ. NKQ OLAWA'V
N WANVGK. NDD GT OLA JNKQP JGWK
OLNO MNV AZAW BNQA MNV BNQA SK
1911.

                        -DAMSV FDNJC

270. QYU JXVVUHUMLU CUQKUUM AUR
DMJ ZNTU XA QYDQ AUR HUZXUTUA
QUMAXNM DMJ ZNTU LDPAUA XQ.

                        -KNNJO DZZUM

271. UCPOCCS POF CIHMV, H JMOJDV
RHKL PXC FSC H SCICE PEHCT UCWFEC.

272. D VGZ ZF MGDPK GZ G HDY D
TZKY BF ZMKGH LKXDMY BXK LGCM GMY
YF MFBXDMO.

—NFXMMA QGCZFM

273. NDL IOD MKIOA. YD'MM MKD
ITJFC MZKLR KV YD GISD CJ. K'N IL
IMRDTOI MKIO. K VKRFOD CYJ RJJP
MKDA NIXD I QJAKCKSD.

—CKN IMMDL

274. EULAVU Q VULZFU PA PWMU TAZV
XZUFPQAHF, Q GWOU WH ADUHQHY
FPWPUNUHP.

275. TA TJQSMV EXR XPXFCRQ TM
HMFCP XC XLQVMRR - KCQFI F
FCQVJGKLMG SMV QJ WVXCD RFCXQVX.

                    —XCPFM GFLDFCRJC

276. HK HS'B SGM OBAEGHE RMSVCYI
VGA FC SGMA RMMF L OGCRM RXTJMY?

                    —YCJHR VHUUHLTB

277. MTB QANCM MALB A CXEW AE MTB
KTINKT KTSAN MYS TIEVNBV JBSJRB
KTXEWBV MTBAN NBRAWASE.

                    —QNBV XRRBE

278. LFRJTJF WD FWHP ZTJQJDTJZ GJB
BPLF FWGP.

-KWFF GPBBPFF

279. PO IGOOR JL IORCXCVO XMMUI,
PO DCEO WJLLOX CRCXV, PO VCFO
IORCXCVO ECQCVJMLI - PO'XO WMJLZ
OEOXAVDJLZ PO QCL VM FOOR MBX
UCXXJCZO VMZOVDOX.

-XMWLOA WCLZOXHJOGW

280. DS PSKR SAR QTVRAD ITZ FR
VROTVLRL TK T IJKMSVDGAR; DS PSKR
FSDE PSSWK PJWR XTVRPRKKARKK.

-SKXTV CJPLR

281. ZPJ KMJ ZPHMT UKX QPKXSFM'Z
FK HQ ZIU ZK ZJSS L ELW FIHDJI PKR
ZK TJZ QKNJRPJIJ.

                        -VHNNU BLSSKM

282. MVOUXEB UEEPMEIBK WDUEF QP
PWBE IYBOEPNTD, QYBXO EMIDBUO
KXFUFQBO FXQB, QP QPMOXFQF. QYBT
FUT XQ'F HMFQ DXVB KXFEBTDUEK,
BCIBWQ QYB 6-JPPQ ZPMFB XF OBUD.

                        -IPEUE P'NOXBE

283. GUJ'Q GQ S XGQ ZJJAKDGJC QNSQ
LFOQFKU OSRR MNSQ QNAB LF
"WKSOQGOA"?

                        -CAFKCA OSKRGJ

105

284. ZIK'V WIDSCV LIVUCD'T ZNX. ID NT VUCX BNYY FV FK JCECDYX UFYYT, ZNZ'T VUFDZ QFWC ZNX.

-HNX YCKI

285. ED E ASJRG KZ VEKJRZ'D KBMH AQMDJDWBG QV WNQ ASQJABD: WEIB JW QF RBECB JW.

-YHGGZ SEAIBWW

286. B RTQ EPTHBKBGL HU CG TCYG HU TJQRGP DPUXDHYW, TJL B LBL. B QTBL B LBLJ'H MJUR.

-XTPM HRTBJ

106

287. UIUMP EJL'N WMUJE CN AD GU
JGFU AD NCLT CLAD AXU JMEN DO J
ZDEJL ZCAXDVA JFND OJFFCLH CLAD
XUM XJLWN.

                        -KUMMP FUZCN

288. Q WTR'P BRTV (QE PYHA VHNH
FHR TN VTFHR EMRJ NGRRQRU RMBHW
MDNTJJ PYH EQHKW). PYHA YMW LMUJ
TXHN PYHQN YHMWJ.

                        -ATUQ LHNNM

289. CV ICV E BIW WI WKIAER VNPRIT
- PO PW CERT'W OIF KPA, CV'N XV
CEWLKPTH WVBVUPRPIT XQ
LETNBVBPHKW.

-APBWIT XVFBV

290. QNQMAOKREF RW XSEEA, DW VHEF
DW RO'W KDJJQEREF OH WHCQGHLA
QVWQ.

-URVV MHFQMW

291. QW'K C BFGGZ WYQGU WYCW DYIG
C TCG YCKG'W CGZWYQGU MG ICPWY WM
DMPPZ CRMFW, YI UMIK MBB CGJ UIWK
TCPPQIJ.

-PMRIPW BPMKW

292. I KILX SM IW XQHXFSXWBX DJO
EICX VSLE IWJLEXF HXFMJW LEIL
PINXM DJO IHHFXBSILX UXSWA IGJWX.

108

-GIFFD KICSK

293. KC EGTR PFB G ERLR DPNNC TAL WERFWC CRPLI. WDRF ER KRW.

-LABFRC BPFURLTGRZB

294. QGD WSGV QGD'XH THLUMHE AYEERH LOH VMHS QGD'TH ULDJYGSHE JG IRGV EGVS CQ QGDT EGUJGT, YSIJHLE GP CQ JMH NGRYUH.

-FGLS TYXHTI

295. BGU QYBUJYUB QL PCLB Z VNJMS DZLLQYF YNBUL ZJNCYS Z HMZLLJNNT.

-PNY LBUVZJB

296. W GDIDP HLPBDE S HSRD — UCE
WG ZLCP RSTD, W'VV UD BVSF EL XSOD
SG DMRDQEWLG.

                          —BPLCRNL XSPM

297. BUGOSEK SNI LDGI. DQ'K EUPN
HDLI QFSQ KPYTK.

                          —NDYTE VINZSDK

298. GDA CEAR RTD FEGD RTQAO LHZG
RTDQH BAVDHCDEH RTER RTDM CEAR
LHZG CZGDA: E IQRRID UQR ZL
FBXXZHR, EAV E IQRRID UQR ZL
LHDDVZG.

-PDHHM FDQALDIV

299. Q PJY YWDDMQLO AVD FAVDS
LQOVA, JWFLD, AVJLBY AF AVD
DEADSUQLJAFS.

-DUF MVQWQMY

300. Q'L CSX P ODFBSC TUS DLGFPKDB
KUPHHDCNDB. Q FRC ZFSL KUPHHDCNDB.
Q GFDPI TSFHM FDKSFMB FRCCQCN ZFSL
KUPHHDCNDB.

-HPFFV MPWQM

111

HINTS

1. O = S   F = N   J = R   Z = O
2. J = M   W = I   C = D   I = G
3. E = B   D = K   G = M   V = G
4. I = U   X = F   A = S   Y = C
5. Z = U   V = T   J = L   S = K
6. B = A   X = M   K = Y   I = W
7. B = N   Y = D   G = U   D = L
8. R = O   S = C   D = M   H = W
9. V = O   J = P   L = S   M = L
10. Y = D   S = P   E = L   I = W
11. J = L   E = N   G = B   T = H
12. D = C   U = R   X = B   H = W
13. Y = I   T = L   G = W   F = O
14. M = R   G = T   H = W   K = X
15. Q = D   I = P   W = G   F = V
16. Y = A   P = L   U = F   I = O
17. S = C   L = R   U = M   O = J
18. E = B   K = N   P = M   L = P
19. O = K   W = R   V = H   Q = M
20. Z = K   Y = M   O = V   B = L
21. T = H   L = G   I = D   B = C
22. N = G   D = Y   K = W   P = I
23. F = C   J = R   Z = G   N = O
24. M = S   U = L   D = P   V = W
25. Q = N   M = W   X = B   E = R

26. T = G	V = C	M = W	G = A
27. Y = W	Q = S	C = D	U = R
28. F = M	X = W	M = C	W = Y
29. C = W	X = P	U = Y	Q = L
30. M = D	F = M	X = B	Z = E
31. L = G	B = P	F = Y	C = D
32. V = T	O = M	Q = P	F = R
33. G = M	N = P	I = G	J = L
34. O = N	V = B	Y = W	J = R
35. X = B	M = L	C = P	U = W
36. R = C	W = M	O = G	L = N
37. X = N	Q = G	P = S	G = J
38. K = W	S = L	J = P	O = M
39. K = E	I = W	Y = R	T = O
40. Z = M	C = W	R = J	I = F
41. H = S	Y = M	W = R	Z = N
42. B = U	G = C	O = P	Y = M
43. Q = F	Y = L	U = C	P = R
44. E = M	Z = C	L = H	G = S
45. W = I	H = F	N = B	R = C
46. I = P	B = Z	O = M	T = S
47. K = F	S = G	E = R	Z = Y
48. Q = T	H = D	A = W	V = I
49. L = A	H = M	Z = G	O = F
50. J = K	Y = C	S = P	Z = R
51. R = D	X = F	U = R	E = Y
52. E = U	H = M	S = N	V = R
53. D = O	B = G	L = N	X = L
54. S = F	E = L	M = Y	Z = B

114

55. O = P	W = M	J = D	B = F
56. U = C	X = G	O = M	Q = R
57. V = R	A = L	O = W	T = P
58. O = R	A = U	G = T	D = P
59. Z = K	T = F	N = D	H = M
60. J = D	X = R	N = C	F = B
61. S = M	L = E	T = L	X = S
62. I = D	N = B	E = P	C = O
63. N = C	Z = D	K = M	Q = N
64. Z = P	C = G	L = R	K = I
65. M = I	S = C	B = R	E = P
66. K = U	M = K	T = B	Y = M
67. D = N	R = M	G = T	X = D
68. M = R	G = C	K = H	J = U
69. V = H	A = S	G = B	K = R
70. W = G	T = U	G = K	Z = W
71. T = S	Q = H	M = D	O = G
72. U = R	A = K	O = L	Y = F
73. Y = S	L = V	H = W	M = E
74. N = V	F = K	T = M	D = S
75. F = D	O = V	C = B	H = C
76. D = K	F = L	H = C	G = M
77. P = U	I = B	N = Y	X = A
78. M = O	G = P	E = B	C = R
79. M = L	D = B	U = G	X = C
80. K = B	P = R	Z = Y	O = F
81. H = T	O = Y	E = W	Q = C
82. P = C	L = G	M = R	G = K
83. F = N	G = L	H = F	J = M

84. T = O   W = S   E = L   U = W
85. F = S   T = L   E = G   N = I
86. S = T   O = C   X = D   Z = Y
87. A = K   U = W   R = E   L = G
88. W = M   Z = W   H = B   G = C
89. Y = D   U = M   N = S   E = H
90. G = M   K = C   Y = D   P = H
91. J = L   Q = D   B = M   D = C
92. T = M   F = G   H = L   D = N
93. B = D   Q = B   Y = M   D = C
94. Q = G   A = X   Z = T   X = H
95. E = V   J = F   K = T   Y = R
96. D = W   V = G   C = P   E = O
97. K = R   X = H   J = D   T = U
98. C = Y   D = B   R = S   V = U
99. O = Y   X = W   G = O   C = H
100. Y = E   G = L   I = F   O = H
101. V = N   D = R   T = G   N = A
102. K = B   H = D   P = O   D = Y
103. I = A   C = M   O = R   K = C
104. T = H   K = R   B = Q   P = S
105. R = P   U = H   T = K   O = R
106. O = M   L = P   Q = I   N = K
107. F = B   H = P   W = L   D = G
108. J = W   A = G   Q = I   E = V
109. A = K   F = R   D = J   Q = F
110. O = G   K = S   V = C   X = Y
111. T = H   O = R   A = K   I = O
112. V = D   R = B   S = R   B = C

113.	T = H	S = C	Z = I	G = O
114.	Q = H	R = P	B = D	S = O
115.	L = P	R = B	Z = G	Y = R
116.	W = E	Q = U	J = B	U = C
117.	F = M	Y = C	Q = N	X = F
118.	D = E	A = G	I = B	Z = I
119.	J = A	K = S	L = O	E = P
120.	E = N	I = F	K = M	J = P
121.	Y = O	M = R	A = Y	C = H
122.	J = N	W = B	P = L	B = J
123.	O = I	P = W	S = F	Z = P
124.	Z = Y	S = B	N = S	E = C
125.	X = G	J = P	T = W	N = O
126.	K = G	N = M	V = L	A = Y
127.	D = U	A = Y	Z = C	O = G
128.	G = Y	K = V	T = W	C = O
129.	N = H	B = R	Y = P	R = N
130.	L = G	I = F	E = P	B = L
131.	L = C	D = Y	J = M	U = D
132.	I = P	F = B	N = I	W = F
133.	Z = O	X = G	W = U	D = W
134.	I = F	C = K	W = G	J = R
135.	H = E	G = C	Y = D	T = M
136.	Y = S	R = V	D = G	H = M
137.	V = M	E = W	D = R	C = F
138.	K = F	Y = W	Q = D	E = S
139.	V = L	T = P	A = H	E = R
140.	M = R	Q = G	Y = P	L = J
141.	H = S	R = B	G = H	X = L

```
142.  G = N      W = M      T = H      R = O
143.  O = I      W = Y      C = F      J = M
144.  E = P      K = F      L = E      Z = N
145.  T = M      E = B      X = Y      P = O
146.  T = F      K = M      G = C      H = R
147.  I = A      J = X      R = B      O = H
148.  U = C      P = K      L = D      M = F
149.  M = W      L = P      N = B      J = S
150.  A = N      X = B      Z = W      I = M
151.  F = B      M = C      T = Y      K = F
152.  L = M      P = B      J = L      M = A
153.  E = L      P = V      A = Y      W = U
154.  O = W      T = M      N = C      R = T
155.  V = O      N = W      I = L      C = D
156.  V = N      F = B      U = O      R = C
157.  I = O      E = M      S = V      B = P
158.  T = P      S = H      Q = B      G = S
159.  C = L      T = B      Q = K      E = R
160.  Z = N      S = L      J = R      O = Y
161.  T = N      J = T      M = B      K = C
162.  H = P      G = M      U = B      E = V
163.  M = I      W = F      Q = L      I = A
164.  O = H      A = L      J = Y      Q = R
165.  W = A      T = H      M = K      G = T
166.  C = I      K = O      M = H      F = K
167.  I = U      B = D      H = S      X = R
168.  V = I      X = B      U = G      J = O
169.  J = R      W = F      G = C      I = W
170.  R = H      V = M      S = D      I = G
```

171.	S	=	G	F	=	Y	Z	=	N	M	=	S
172.	T	=	H	I	=	F	Q	=	G	K	=	E
173.	O	=	M	X	=	C	N	=	U	Q	=	E
174.	E	=	G	O	=	M	S	=	P	F	=	L
175.	Z	=	E	M	=	F	X	=	O	W	=	D
176.	K	=	E	D	=	B	X	=	D	I	=	W
177.	G	=	N	K	=	Y	I	=	G	X	=	S
178.	L	=	T	B	=	L	S	=	R	Q	=	B
179.	X	=	Y	U	=	L	S	=	N	Y	=	A
180.	K	=	G	D	=	Y	V	=	B	R	=	P
181.	X	=	J	L	=	W	C	=	F	S	=	R
182.	I	=	D	J	=	W	S	=	J	C	=	F
183.	T	=	L	S	=	C	B	=	D	R	=	O
184.	J	=	S	F	=	M	K	=	L	D	=	O
185.	D	=	C	S	=	M	Q	=	V	R	=	H
186.	D	=	T	X	=	R	O	=	B	G	=	M
187.	C	=	L	W	=	O	J	=	N	T	=	W
188.	C	=	R	A	=	W	M	=	Y	U	=	L
189.	S	=	R	U	=	L	B	=	Y	I	=	F
190.	L	=	F	S	=	C	C	=	K	N	=	D
191.	R	=	S	I	=	N	Z	=	R	D	=	L
192.	V	=	E	J	=	M	C	=	V	O	=	L
193.	D	=	A	H	=	G	S	=	E	B	=	P
194.	M	=	L	R	=	H	C	=	K	W	=	P
195.	W	=	T	Z	=	Y	I	=	G	K	=	L
196.	Z	=	D	O	=	P	M	=	F	S	=	C
197.	U	=	S	L	=	D	Z	=	R	B	=	O
198.	Z	=	R	X	=	W	V	=	H	C	=	T
199.	W	=	A	E	=	F	A	=	T	F	=	M

200.	Q = F	J = K	N = L	U = D
201.	Z = Y	L = E	B = N	X = D
202.	J = G	M = F	Z = C	E = B
203.	U = A	C = B	N = D	M = W
204.	R = A	Q = M	V = G	I = B
205.	M = R	L = I	O = M	S = O
206.	X = M	S = C	G = P	B = L
207.	M = S	B = C	D = L	Z = P
208.	N = C	B = M	P = W	F = B
209.	V = M	A = W	D = R	M = A
210.	K = L	P = F	Z = M	L = C
211.	P = C	G = N	Q = O	S = K
212.	G = W	F = P	K = G	S = N
213.	V = D	R = B	E = L	B = M
214.	G = R	K = O	P = C	H = K
215.	V = Y	S = R	O = G	P = H
216.	T = W	M = D	Q = S	B = I
217.	H = W	Z = C	Q = Y	X = B
218.	J = L	N = C	H = O	M = W
219.	W = N	X = U	C = W	R = S
220.	B = H	F = B	E = L	R = E
221.	W = R	X = C	S = B	I = M
222.	R = T	N = P	B = R	E = L
223.	L = P	E = M	Q = H	D = W
224.	W = F	M = D	O = I	T = E
225.	L = C	J = B	M = S	C = H
226.	O = I	U = G	V = H	D = M
227.	V = I	R = M	B = C	W = B
228.	B = P	N = W	I = S	P = R

```
229.  H = O      R = W      Z = M      P = T
230.  S = C      E = P      Q = D      A = M
231.  S = R      O = G      L = C      Y = V
232.  X = O      T = R      J = H      C = D
233.  I = Y      C = D      B = H      W = R
234.  U = D      X = L      G = O      V = I
235.  K = Y      G = K      I = W      Q = G
236.  C = I      L = H      B = W      H = C
237.  N = L      F = S      R = O      U = F
238.  R = U      I = P      E = R      B = G
239.  L = R      F = H      A = M      D = F
240.  I = E      F = P      G = R      U = S
241.  C = L      D = M      Z = V      F = N
242.  V = W      D = F      O = C      P = L
243.  G = A      K = P      Q = B      X = F
244.  Q = N      I = P      R = C      T = G
245.  D = M      J = P      M = B      K = R
246.  K = A      X = J      C = G      T = M
247.  O = L      C = B      V = P      A = O
248.  V = E      I = M      W = D      S = T
249.  H = C      D = S      U = P      S = V
250.  B = L      Y = H      N = W      D = M
251.  Y = C      U = F      N = D      Z = Y
252.  G = S      V = D      H = L      A = Y
253.  R = N      W = L      Z = O      P = R
254.  Y = I      C = R      P = H      T = O
255.  Z = O      U = H      L = U      A = L
256.  Z = Y      S = P      R = D      U = M
257.  J = O      D = M      P = R      O = G
```

258. O = C	V = L	X = M	N = R
259. S = L	H = G	N = K	D = I
260. L = H	B = P	I = D	J = C
261. Y = U	P = G	V = T	E = D
262. P = W	B = K	J = R	W = N
263. E = Y	W = C	X = R	Z = O
264. X = B	F = L	V = I	L = R
265. B = T	C = W	L = B	Q = S
266. T = V	Q = N	H = L	J = S
267. P = B	A = R	V = Y	U = A
268. B = H	Y = M	W = L	G = V
269. N = A	J = C	L = H	Z = V
270. J = D	Z = L	X = I	T = V
271. M = L	O = W	E = R	I = V
272. L = B	Y = D	H = K	M = N
273. N = M	K = I	R = G	M = L
274. L = F	A = O	V = R	P = T
275. S = H	L = C	P = G	T = M
276. V = W	Y = R	O = P	J = B
277. T = H	Q = F	R = L	W = G
278. F = L	Z = P	L = A	B = R
279. Q = C	E = V	W = D	O = E
280. D = T	P = L	V = R	F = B
281. S = L	N = M	I = R	M = N
282. M = U	T = Y	N = B	X = I
283. U = S	J = N	K = R	O = C
284. K = N	U = H	W = F	D = R
285. B = E	I = K	A = C	K = M
286. H = T	R = W	Q = S	D = P

287. M = R   E = M   X = H   D = O
288. F = M   B = K   A = Y   L = B
289. V = E   X = B   N = D   B = L
290. W = S   M = R   F = G   E = N
291. B = F   G = N   P = R   U = G
292. S = I   H = P   F = R   K = D
293. N = P   E = W   B = D   W = T
294. R = L   U = C   T = R   D = U
295. L = S   V = W   Q = I   J = R
296. H = F   R = C   G = N   M = X
297. K = S   Y = C   T = K   E = Y
298. D = E   L = F   I = L   U = B
299. L = N   M = P   V = H   W = L
300. K = C   F = R   H = L   N = G

ANSWERS

1. TWO THINGS ARE INFINITE: THE UNIVERSE AND HUMAN STUPIDITY; AND I'M NOT SURE ABOUT THE UNIVERSE.
-ALBERT EINSTEIN

2. HAVE YOU EVER NOTICED THAT ANYBODY DRIVING SLOWER THAN YOU IS AN IDIOT, AND ANYONE GOING FASTER THAN YOU IS A MANIAC?
-GEORGE CARLIN

3. I DON'T KNOW WHAT'S MORE EXHAUSTING ABOUT PARENTING: THE GETTING UP EARLY, OR THE ACTING LIKE YOU KNOW WHAT YOU'RE DOING.
-JIM GAFFIGAN

4. YOU CANNOT CORRECT AN OLD PERSON EVERY TIME THEY SAY SOMETHING OFFENSIVE. YOU WOULD NEVER MAKE IT THROUGH THANKSGIVING DINNER.
-STEPHEN COLBERT

5. THE ONLY WAY TO KEEP YOUR HEALTH IS TO EAT WHAT YOU DON'T WANT, DRINK WHAT YOU DON'T LIKE, AND DO WHAT YOU'D RATHER NOT.
-MARK TWAIN

6. NOT ALL CHEMICALS ARE BAD. WITHOUT CHEMICALS SUCH AS HYDROGEN AND OXYGEN FOR EXAMPLE, THERE WOULD BE NO WAY TO MAKE WATER, A VITAL INGREDIENT IN BEER.
-DAVE BARRY

7. IF WHAT YOU'VE DONE IS STUPID BUT IT WORKS, THEN IT REALLY ISN'T THAT STUPID AT ALL.
-DAVID LETTERMAN

8. BEFORE YOU CRITICIZE A MAN, WALK A MILE IN HIS SHOES. THAT WAY, WHEN YOU DO CRITICIZE HIM, YOU'LL BE A MILE AWAY AND HAVE HIS SHOES.
-STEVE MARTIN

9. PEOPLE SAY NOTHING IS IMPOSSIBLE, BUT I DO NOTHING EVERY DAY.
-A. A. MILNE

10. I DON'T HAVE PET PEEVES LIKE SOME PEOPLE. I HAVE WHOLE KENNELS OF IRRITATION.
-WHOOPI GOLDBERG

11. TROUBLE KNOCKED AT THE DOOR, BUT, HEARING LAUGHTER, HURRIED AWAY.
-BENJAMIN FRANKLIN

12. RECESSION IS WHEN A NEIGHBOR LOSES HIS JOB. DEPRESSION IS WHEN YOU LOSE YOURS.
-RONALD REAGAN

13. A WOMAN IS LIKE A TEA BAG - YOU CAN'T TELL HOW STRONG SHE IS UNTIL YOU PUT HER IN HOT WATER.
-ELEANOR ROOSEVELT

14. IF A WOMAN TELLS YOU SHE'S TWENTY AND LOOKS SIXTEEN, SHE'S TWELVE. IF SHE TELLS YOU SHE'S TWENTY-SIX AND LOOKS TWENTY-SIX, SHE'S DAMN NEAR FORTY.
-CHRIS ROCK

15. IF YOU LIVE TO BE ONE HUNDRED, YOU'VE GOT IT MADE. VERY FEW PEOPLE DIE PAST THAT AGE.
-GEORGE BURNS

16. BETTER TO REMAIN SILENT AND BE THOUGHT A FOOL THAN TO SPEAK OUT AND REMOVE ALL DOUBT.
-ABRAHAM LINCOLN

17. I REFUSE TO JOIN ANY CLUB THAT WOULD HAVE ME AS A MEMBER.
-GROUCHO MARX

18. A BANK IS A PLACE THAT WILL LEND YOU MONEY IF YOU CAN PROVE THAT YOU DON'T NEED IT.
-BOB HOPE

19. LIFE MOVES PRETTY FAST. IF YOU DON'T STOP AND LOOK AROUND ONCE IN A WHILE, YOU COULD MISS IT.
-JOHN HUGHES

20. IF EVOLUTION REALLY WORKS, HOW COME MOTHERS ONLY HAVE TWO HANDS?
-MILTON BERLE

21. HE WHO LAUGHS LAST DIDN'T GET THE JOKE.
-CHARLES DE GAULLE

22. ALWAYS FORGIVE YOUR ENEMIES - NOTHING ANNOYS THEM SO MUCH.
-OSCAR WILDE

23. THE AVERAGE DOG IS A NICER PERSON THAN THE AVERAGE PERSON.
-ANDY ROONEY

24. WE SPEND THE FIRST TWELVE MONTHS OF OUR CHILDREN'S LIVES TEACHING THEM TO WALK AND TALK AND THE NEXT TWELVE TELLING THEM TO SIT DOWN AND SHUT UP.
-PHYLLIS DILLER

25. WHY DO THEY CALL IT RUSH HOUR WHEN NOTHING MOVES?
-ROBIN WILLIAMS

26. DON'T WORRY ABOUT THE WORLD COMING TO AN END TODAY. IT IS ALREADY TOMORROW IN AUSTRALIA.
-CHARLES M. SCHULZ

27. I REFUSE TO ANSWER THAT QUESTION ON THE GROUNDS THAT I DON'T KNOW THE ANSWER.
-DOUGLAS ADAMS

28. I DON'T WANT TO ACHIEVE IMMORTALITY THROUGH MY WORK. I WANT TO ACHIEVE IT THROUGH NOT DYING.
-WOODY ALLEN

29. NEVER FOLLOW ANYONE ELSE'S PATH. UNLESS YOU'RE IN THE WOODS AND YOU'RE LOST AND YOU SEE A PATH. THEN BY ALL MEANS FOLLOW THAT PATH.
-ELLEN DEGENERES

30. SEIZE THE MOMENT. REMEMBER ALL THOSE WOMEN ON THE "TITANIC" WHO WAVED OFF THE DESSERT CART.
-ERMA BOMBECK

31. MY PSYCHIATRIST TOLD ME I WAS CRAZY AND I SAID I WANT A SECOND OPINION. HE SAID OKAY, YOU'RE UGLY TOO.
-RODNEY DANGERFIELD

32. WHOEVER SAID MONEY CAN'T BUY HAPPINESS DIDN'T KNOW WHERE TO SHOP.
-GERTRUDE STEIN

33. WHEN I DIE, I WANT TO DIE LIKE MY GRANDFATHER WHO DIED PEACEFULLY IN HIS SLEEP. NOT SCREAMING LIKE ALL THE PASSENGERS IN HIS CAR.
-WILL ROGERS

34. IF THERE WERE NO BAD PEOPLE, THERE WOULD BE NO GOOD LAWYERS.
-CHARLES DICKENS

35. ALWAYS GO TO OTHER PEOPLE'S FUNERALS, OTHERWISE THEY WON'T COME TO YOURS.
-YOGI BERRA

36. I WAS THINKING ABOUT HOW PEOPLE SEEM TO READ THE BIBLE A WHOLE LOT MORE AS THEY GET OLDER; THEN IT DAWNED ON ME - THEY'RE CRAMMING FOR THEIR FINAL EXAM.
-GEORGE CARLIN

37. THE FIRST TIME I SEE A JOGGER SMILING, I'LL CONSIDER IT.
-JOAN RIVERS

38. I'D LIKE TO LIVE LIKE A POOR MAN - ONLY WITH LOTS OF MONEY.
-PABLO PICASSO

39. WHAT'S ANOTHER WORD FOR THESAURUS?
-STEVEN WRIGHT

40. NEVER PUT OFF TILL TOMORROW WHAT YOU CAN DO THE DAY AFTER TOMORROW JUST AS WELL.
-MARK TWAIN

41. THEY SAY MARRIAGES ARE MADE IN HEAVEN. BUT SO IS THUNDER AND LIGHTNING.
-CLINT EASTWOOD

42. PARENTING IS A CULT. AND AS A CULT MEMBER, YOU CAN TRY TO EXPLAIN IT TO OTHER PEOPLE, BUT WE JUST APPEAR LIKE LUNATICS.
-JIM GAFFIGAN

43. IF ANY OF YOU CRY AT MY FUNERAL I'LL NEVER SPEAK TO YOU AGAIN.
-STAN LAUREL

44. THERE CANNOT BE A CRISIS NEXT WEEK. MY
SCHEDULE IS ALREADY FULL.
-HENRY KISSINGER

45. MY THERAPIST TOLD ME THE WAY TO ACHIEVE
TRUE INNER PEACE IS TO FINISH WHAT I START. SO
FAR I'VE FINISHED TWO BAGS OF M&MS AND A
CHOCOLATE CAKE. I FEEL BETTER ALREADY.
-DAVE BARRY

46. A MAN IN LOVE IS INCOMPLETE UNTIL HE IS
MARRIED. THEN HE'S FINISHED.
-ZSA ZSA GABOR

47. PEOPLE IN L.A. ARE DEATHLY AFRAID OF
GLUTEN. I SWEAR TO GOD, YOU COULD ROB A LIQUOR
STORE IN THIS CITY WITH A BAGEL.
-RYAN REYNOLDS

48. I COOK WITH WINE, SOMETIMES I EVEN ADD IT
TO THE FOOD.
-W. C. FIELDS

49. THE MOST TERRIFYING WORDS IN THE ENGLISH
LANGUAGE ARE: I'M FROM THE GOVERNMENT AND I'M
HERE TO HELP.
-RONALD REAGAN

50. DON'T CRY OVER SPILLED MILK. BY THIS TIME TOMORROW, IT'LL BE FREE YOGURT.
-STEPHEN COLBERT

51. ANYONE CAN BE CONFIDENT WITH A FULL HEAD OF HAIR. BUT A CONFIDENT BALD MAN - THERE'S YOUR DIAMOND IN THE ROUGH.
-LARRY DAVID

52. BEFORE YOU MARRY A PERSON, YOU SHOULD FIRST MAKE THEM USE A COMPUTER WITH SLOW INTERNET TO SEE WHO THEY REALLY ARE.
-WILL FERRELL

53. I LOVE BEING MARRIED. IT'S SO GREAT TO FIND THAT ONE SPECIAL PERSON YOU WANT TO ANNOY FOR THE REST OF YOUR LIFE.
-RITA RUDNER

54. A TWO-YEAR OLD IS KIND OF LIKE A BLENDER, BUT YOU DON'T HAVE ANY TOP FOR IT.
-JERRY SEINFELD

55. IT'S MUCH EASIER FOR ME TO MAKE MAJOR LIFE, MULTI-MILLION DOLLAR DECISIONS, THAN IT IS TO DECIDE ON A CARPET FOR MY FRONT PORCH. THAT'S THE TRUTH.
-OPRAH WINFREY

56. MARRIAGE IS THE CHIEF CAUSE OF DIVORCE.
-GROUCHO MARX

57. I LIKE LONG WALKS, ESPECIALLY WHEN THEY
ARE TAKEN BY PEOPLE WHO ANNOY ME.
-NOEL COWARD

58. AT EVERY PARTY THERE ARE TWO KINDS OF
PEOPLE - THOSE WHO WANT TO GO HOME AND THOSE
WHO DON'T. THE TROUBLE IS, THEY ARE USUALLY
MARRIED TO EACH OTHER.
-ANN LANDERS

59. WHEN I WAS A KID MY PARENTS MOVED A LOT,
BUT I ALWAYS FOUND THEM.
-RODNEY DANGERFIELD

60. I DON'T BELIEVE IN ASTROLOGY; I'M A
SAGITTARIUS AND WE'RE SKEPTICAL.
-ARTHUR C. CLARKE

61. I NEVER FEEL MORE ALONE THAN WHEN I'M
TRYING TO PUT SUNSCREEN ON MY BACK.
-JIMMY KIMMEL

62. FACEBOOK JUST SOUNDS LIKE A DRAG. IN MY
DAY SEEING PICTURES OF PEOPLES VACATIONS WAS
CONSIDERED A PUNISHMENT.
-BETTY WHITE

63. MARRIAGE IS LIKE MUSHROOMS: WE NOTICE TOO LATE IF THEY ARE GOOD OR BAD.
-WOODY ALLEN

64. GRAVITATION CAN NOT BE HELD RESPONSIBLE FOR PEOPLE FALLING IN LOVE.
-ALBERT EINSTEIN

65. STARBUCKS SAYS THEY ARE GOING TO START PUTTING RELIGIOUS QUOTES ON CUPS. THE VERY FIRST ONE WILL SAY, "JESUS! THIS CUP IS EXPENSIVE!"
-CONAN O'BRIEN

66. A COMPUTER ONCE BEAT ME AT CHESS, BUT IT WAS NO MATCH FOR ME AT KICK BOXING.
-EMO PHILIPS

67. I DRINK TO MAKE OTHER PEOPLE MORE INTERESTING.
-ERNEST HEMINGWAY

68. TO THOSE OF YOU WHO RECEIVED HONOURS, AWARDS AND DISTINCTIONS, I SAY WELL DONE. AND TO THE C STUDENTS, I SAY YOU, TOO, CAN BE PRESIDENT OF THE UNITED STATES.
-GEORGE W. BUSH

69. IT'S A RECESSION WHEN YOUR NEIGHBOR LOSES HIS JOB; IT'S A DEPRESSION WHEN YOU LOSE YOURS.
-HARRY S. TRUMAN

70. DON'T KEEP A MAN GUESSING TOO LONG - HE'S SURE TO FIND THE ANSWER SOMEWHERE ELSE.
-MAE WEST

71. THERE SHOULD BE A CHILDREN'S SONG: "IF YOU'RE HAPPY AND YOU KNOW IT, KEEP IT TO YOURSELF AND LET YOUR DAD SLEEP."
-JIM GAFFIGAN

72. IF I WANT TO KNOCK A STORY OFF THE FRONT PAGE, I JUST CHANGE MY HAIRSTYLE.
-HILLARY CLINTON

73. PEOPLE WHO THINK THEY KNOW EVERYTHING ARE A GREAT ANNOYANCE TO THOSE OF US WHO DO.
-ISAAC ASIMOV

74. I SHOULD BE A POSTAGE STAMP. THAT'S THE ONLY WAY I'LL EVER GET LICKED.
-MUHAMMAD ALI

75. MY WIFE MARY AND I HAVE BEEN MARRIED FOR FORTY-SEVEN YEARS AND NOT ONCE HAVE WE HAD AN ARGUMENT SERIOUS ENOUGH TO CONSIDER DIVORCE; MURDER, YES, BUT DIVORCE, NEVER.
-JACK BENNY

76. CLOTHES MAKE THE MAN. NAKED PEOPLE HAVE LITTLE OR NO INFLUENCE IN SOCIETY.
-MARK TWAIN

77. THE SECRET OF STAYING YOUNG IS TO LIVE HONESTLY, EAT SLOWLY, AND LIE ABOUT YOUR AGE.
-LUCILLE BALL

78. POLITICS IS NOT A BAD PROFESSION. IF YOU SUCCEED THERE ARE MANY REWARDS, IF YOU DISGRACE YOURSELF YOU CAN ALWAYS WRITE A BOOK.
-RONALD REAGAN

79. ACCORDING TO A NEW SURVEY, 90% OF MEN SAY THEIR LOVER IS ALSO THEIR BEST FRIEND. WHICH IS REALLY KIND OF DISTURBING WHEN YOU CONSIDER MAN'S BEST FRIEND IS HIS DOG.
-JAY LENO

80. IF YOU COME TO A FORK IN THE ROAD, TAKE IT.
-YOGI BERRA

81. HERE'S AN EASY WAY TO FIGURE OUT IF YOU'RE IN A CULT: IF YOU'RE WONDERING WHETHER YOU'RE IN A CULT, THE ANSWER IS YES.
-STEPHEN COLBERT

82. TRUE TERROR IS TO WAKE UP ONE MORNING AND DISCOVER THAT YOUR HIGH SCHOOL CLASS IS RUNNING THE COUNTRY.
-KURT VONNEGUT

83. A SUCCESSFUL MAN IS ONE WHO MAKES MORE MONEY THAN HIS WIFE CAN SPEND. A SUCCESSFUL WOMAN IS ONE WHO CAN FIND SUCH A MAN.
-LANA TURNER

84. I ALWAYS WANTED TO BE SOMEBODY, BUT NOW I REALIZE I SHOULD HAVE BEEN MORE SPECIFIC.
-LILY TOMLIN

85. IF STUPIDITY GOT US INTO THIS MESS, THEN WHY CAN'T IT GET US OUT?
-WILL ROGERS

86. MY THEORY IS THAT ALL OF SCOTTISH CUISINE IS BASED ON A DARE.
-MIKE MYERS

87. I'M WRITING A BOOK. I'VE GOT THE PAGE
NUMBERS DONE.
-STEVEN WRIGHT

88. THE ONLY TIME A WOMAN REALLY SUCCEEDS IN
CHANGING A MAN IS WHEN HE IS A BABY.
-NATALIE WOOD

89. HERE'S ALL YOU HAVE TO KNOW ABOUT MEN AND
WOMEN: WOMEN ARE CRAZY, MEN ARE STUPID. AND
THE MAIN REASON WOMEN ARE CRAZY IS THAT MEN
ARE STUPID.
-GEORGE CARLIN

90. SOME CAUSE HAPPINESS WHEREVER THEY GO;
OTHERS WHENEVER THEY GO.
-OSCAR WILDE

91. I DREAM OF A BETTER TOMORROW, WHERE
CHICKENS CAN CROSS THE ROAD AND NOT BE
QUESTIONED ABOUT THEIR MOTIVES.
-RALPH WALDO EMERSON

92. WHY DON'T THEY GIVE US THINGS WE CAN
ACTUALLY USE? I DON'T NEED A THINNER PHONE.
YOU KNOW WHAT I NEED? I NEED A TORTILLA CHIP
THAT CAN SUPPORT THE WEIGHT OF GUACAMOLE.
-ELLEN DEGENERES

93. YOU CAN ONLY BE YOUNG ONCE. BUT YOU CAN ALWAYS BE IMMATURE.
-DAVE BARRY

94. HEALTH NUTS ARE GOING TO FEEL STUPID SOMEDAY, LYING IN HOSPITALS DYING OF NOTHING.
-REDD FOXX

95. BY WORKING FAITHFULLY EIGHT HOURS A DAY YOU MAY EVENTUALLY GET TO BE BOSS AND WORK TWELVE HOURS A DAY.
-ROBERT FROST

96. IF YOU WANT TO MAKE GOD LAUGH, TELL HIM ABOUT YOUR PLANS.
-WOODY ALLEN

97. I HAD A WONDERFUL CHILDHOOD, WHICH IS TOUGH BECAUSE IT'S HARD TO ADJUST TO A MISERABLE ADULTHOOD.
-LARRY DAVID

98. THE HUMAN BRAIN IS SPECIAL. IT STARTS WORKING AS SOON AS YOU GET UP AND IT DOESN'T STOP UNTIL YOU GET TO SCHOOL.
-MILTON BERLE

99. WHEN YOU'RE IN LOVE IT'S THE MOST GLORIOUS TWO AND A HALF DAYS OF YOUR LIFE.
-RICHARD LEWIS

100. I BELIEVE THAT IF LIFE GIVES YOU LEMONS, YOU SHOULD MAKE LEMONADE… AND TRY TO FIND SOMEBODY WHOSE LIFE HAS GIVEN THEM VODKA, AND HAVE A PARTY.
-RON WHITE

101. I FIND TELEVISION VERY EDUCATING. EVERY TIME SOMEBODY TURNS ON THE SET, I GO INTO THE OTHER ROOM AND READ A BOOK.
-GROUCHO MARX

102. I DON'T THINK ANYONE SHOULD WRITE THEIR AUTOBIOGRAPHY UNTIL AFTER THEY'RE DEAD.
-SAMUEL GOLDWYN

103. TALKING ABOUT MUSIC IS LIKE DANCING ABOUT ARCHITECTURE.
-STEVE MARTIN

104. STATUS QUO, YOU KNOW, IS LATIN FOR "THE MESS WE'RE IN".
-RONALD REAGAN

105. I KNOW A MAN WHO GAVE UP SMOKING, DRINKING, SEX, AND RICH FOOD. HE WAS HEALTHY RIGHT UP TO THE DAY HE KILLED HIMSELF.
-JOHNNY CARSON

106. CROCODILES ARE EASY. THEY TRY TO KILL AND EAT YOU. PEOPLE ARE HARDER. SOMETIMES THEY PRETEND TO BE YOUR FRIEND FIRST.
-STEVE IRWIN

107. NEVER GO TO BED MAD. STAY UP AND FIGHT.
-PHYLLIS DILLER

108. NEVER PICK A FIGHT WITH AN UGLY PERSON, THEY'VE GOT NOTHING TO LOSE.
-ROBIN WILLIAMS

109. RAISING KIDS MAY BE A THANKLESS JOB WITH RIDICULOUS HOURS, BUT AT LEAST THE PAY SUCKS.
-JIM GAFFIGAN

110. THERE'S NO SUCH THING AS SOY MILK. IT'S SOY JUICE.
-LEWIS BLACK

111. IF YOU COULD KICK THE PERSON IN THE PANTS RESPONSIBLE FOR MOST OF YOUR TROUBLE, YOU WOULDN'T SIT FOR A MONTH.
-THEODORE ROOSEVELT

112. NEVER GO TO A DOCTOR WHOSE OFFICE PLANTS HAVE DIED.
-ERMA BOMBECK

113. A GOOD SPEECH SHOULD BE LIKE A WOMAN'S SKIRT: LONG ENOUGH TO COVER THE SUBJECT AND SHORT ENOUGH TO CREATE INTEREST.
-WINSTON CHURCHILL

114. THE WORLD TODAY DOESN'T MAKE SENSE, SO WHY SHOULD I PAINT PICTURES THAT DO?
-PABLO PICASSO

115. ONE OF THE GREAT THINGS ABOUT BOOKS IS SOMETIMES THERE ARE SOME FANTASTIC PICTURES.
-GEORGE W. BUSH

116. THE BEST WAY TO TEACH YOUR KIDS ABOUT TAXES IS BY EATING 30 PERCENT OF THEIR ICE CREAM.
-BILL MURRAY

117. MY ESTEEM IN THIS COUNTRY HAS GONE UP SUBSTANTIALLY. IT IS VERY NICE NOW THAT WHEN PEOPLE WAVE AT ME, THEY USE ALL THEIR FINGERS.
-JIMMY CARTER

118. YOU'VE GOT TO BE VERY CAREFUL IF YOU DON'T KNOW WHERE YOU ARE GOING, BECAUSE YOU MIGHT NOT GET THERE.
-YOGI BERRA

119. READER, SUPPOSE YOU WERE AN IDIOT. AND SUPPOSE YOU WERE A MEMBER OF CONGRESS. BUT I REPEAT MYSELF.
-MARK TWAIN

120. LOTS OF PEOPLE WANT TO RIDE WITH YOU IN THE LIMO, BUT WHAT YOU WANT IS SOMEONE WHO WILL TAKE THE BUS WITH YOU WHEN THE LIMO BREAKS DOWN.
-OPRAH WINFREY

121. I TOLD MY PSYCHIATRIST THAT EVERYONE HATES ME. HE SAID I WAS BEING RIDICULOUS - EVERYONE HASN'T MET ME YET.
-RODNEY DANGERFIELD

122. MY BEST BIRTH CONTROL NOW IS JUST TO LEAVE THE LIGHTS ON.
-JOAN RIVERS

123. IT'S AMAZING THAT THE AMOUNT OF NEWS THAT HAPPENS IN THE WORLD EVERY DAY ALWAYS JUST EXACTLY FITS THE NEWSPAPER.
-JERRY SEINFELD

124. TODAY, POSSIBLE PRESIDENTIAL CANDIDATE DONALD TRUMP RELEASED HIS BIRTH CERTIFICATE. IT LISTS HIS EYES AS BLUE AND HIS HAIR AS RIDICULOUS.
-CONAN O'BRIEN

125. NOW, FOR MY YOUNGER VIEWERS OUT THERE, A BOOK IS SOMETHING WE USED TO HAVE BEFORE THE INTERNET. IT'S SORT OF A BLOG FOR PEOPLE WITH ATTENTION SPANS.
-STEPHEN COLBERT

126. IF YOU'RE GOING TO DO SOMETHING TONIGHT THAT YOU'LL BE SORRY FOR TOMORROW MORNING, SLEEP LATE.
-HENNY YOUNGMAN

127. ALL RIGHT EVERYONE, LINE UP ALPHABETICALLY ACCORDING TO YOUR HEIGHT.
-CASEY STENGEL

128. I BELIEVE THERE IS SOMETHING OUT THERE WATCHING US. UNFORTUNATELY, IT'S THE GOVERNMENT.
-WOODY ALLEN

129. THINK OF HOW STUPID THE AVERAGE PERSON IS, AND REALIZE HALF OF THEM ARE STUPIDER THAN THAT.
-GEORGE CARLIN

130. CALIFORNIA IS A FINE PLACE TO LIVE - IF YOU HAPPEN TO BE AN ORANGE.
-FRED ALLEN

131. THE MOST INEFFECTIVE WORKERS ARE SYSTEMATICALLY MOVED TO THE PLACE WHERE THEY CAN DO THE LEAST DAMAGE: MANAGEMENT.
-SCOTT ADAMS

132. IF THIS IS COFFEE, PLEASE BRING ME SOME TEA; BUT IF THIS IS TEA, PLEASE BRING ME SOME COFFEE.
-ABRAHAM LINCOLN

133. YOU KNOW YOU'RE GETTING OLD WHEN YOU STOOP TO TIE YOUR SHOELACES AND WONDER WHAT ELSE YOU COULD DO WHILE YOU'RE DOWN THERE.
-GEORGE BURNS

134. IT'S TRUE HARD WORK NEVER KILLED ANYBODY, BUT I FIGURE, WHY TAKE THE CHANCE?
-RONALD REAGAN

135. IT JUST OCCURRED TO ME THAT THE MAJORITY OF MY DIET IS MADE UP OF THE FOODS THAT MY KID DIDN'T FINISH.
-CARRIE UNDERWOOD

136. WHENEVER SOMEONE CALLS ME UGLY I GET SUPER SAD AND HUG THEM, BECAUSE I KNOW HOW TOUGH LIFE IS FOR THE VISUALLY IMPAIRED.
-WILL FERRELL

137. I WENT TO A RESTAURANT THAT SERVES "BREAKFAST AT ANY TIME". SO I ORDERED FRENCH TOAST DURING THE RENAISSANCE.
-STEVEN WRIGHT

138. I USED TO BE SNOW WHITE, BUT I DRIFTED.
-MAE WEST

139. WHEN YOUR CHILDREN ARE TEENAGERS, IT'S IMPORTANT TO HAVE A DOG SO THAT SOMEONE IN THE HOUSE IS HAPPY TO SEE YOU.
-NORA EPHRON

140. EVERYTHING IS CHANGING. PEOPLE ARE TAKING THE COMEDIANS SERIOUSLY AND THE POLITICIANS AS A JOKE.
-WILL ROGERS

141. OBVIOUSLY, IF I WAS SERIOUS ABOUT HAVING A RELATIONSHIP WITH SOMEONE LONG-TERM, THE LAST PEOPLE I WOULD INTRODUCE HIM TO WOULD BE MY FAMILY.
-CHELSEA HANDLER

142. IF THEY CAN MAKE PENICILLIN OUT OF MOLDY BREAD, THEY CAN SURE MAKE SOMETHING OUT OF YOU.
-MUHAMMAD ALI

143. MY 4 YEAR OLD SON GAVE ME A HAND MADE CARD FOR FATHER'S DAY. MAYBE FOR CHRISTMAS I'LL DRAW HIM A PICTURE OF SOME TOYS.
-JIM GAFFIGAN

144. THE DIFFERENCE BETWEEN STUPIDITY AND GENIUS IS THAT GENIUS HAS ITS LIMITS.
-ALBERT EINSTEIN

145. MY BROTHER IS GAY AND MY PARENTS DON'T CARE, AS LONG AS HE MARRIES A DOCTOR.
-ELAYNE BOOSLER

146. EIGHTY PERCENT OF MARRIED MEN CHEAT IN AMERICA. THE REST CHEAT IN EUROPE.
-JACKIE MASON

147. WHEN YOU'RE IN JAIL, A GOOD FRIEND WILL BE TRYING TO BAIL YOU OUT. A BEST FRIEND WILL BE IN THE CELL NEXT TO YOU SAYING, "DAMN, THAT WAS FUN".
-GROUCHO MARX

148. I CAME FROM A REAL TOUGH NEIGHBORHOOD. ONCE A GUY PULLED A KNIFE ON ME. I KNEW HE WASN'T A PROFESSIONAL, THE KNIFE HAD BUTTER ON IT.
-RODNEY DANGERFIELD

149. I ASKED GOD FOR A BIKE, BUT I KNOW GOD DOESN'T WORK THAT WAY. SO I STOLE A BIKE AND ASKED FOR FORGIVENESS.
-EMO PHILIPS

150. ALWAYS BORROW MONEY FROM A PESSIMIST. HE WON'T EXPECT IT BACK.
-OSCAR WILDE

151. IT IS A SCIENTIFIC FACT THAT YOUR BODY WILL NOT ABSORB CHOLESTEROL IF YOU TAKE IT FROM ANOTHER PERSON'S PLATE.
-DAVE BARRY

152. MY POINT IS, LIFE IS ABOUT BALANCE. THE GOOD AND THE BAD. THE HIGHS AND THE LOWS. THE PINA AND THE COLADA.
-ELLEN DEGENERES

153. ACTUALLY I WALK AROUND WITH THE EMMY WHEREVER I GO, BUT I'M VERY CASUAL ABOUT IT.
-LARRY DAVID

154. THERE ARE ONLY THREE THINGS WOMEN NEED IN LIFE: FOOD, WATER AND COMPLIMENTS.
-CHRIS ROCK

155. I'M NOT AFRAID OF DEATH; I JUST DON'T WANT TO BE THERE WHEN IT HAPPENS.
-WOODY ALLEN

156. YOU CAN OBSERVE A LOT BY JUST WATCHING.
-YOGI BERRA

157. THEY SAY LOVE IS MORE IMPORTANT THAN MONEY… HAVE YOU TRIED PAYING YOUR BILLS WITH A HUG?
-DAVE CHAPPELLE

158. I GREW UP WITH SIX BROTHERS. THAT'S HOW I LEARNED TO DANCE: WAITING FOR THE BATHROOM.
-BOB HOPE

159. THE PROBLEM WITH LIFE IS, BY THE TIME YOU CAN READ WOMEN LIKE A BOOK, YOUR LIBRARY CARD HAS EXPIRED.
-MILTON BERLE

160. THANK YOU, HORSERADISH, FOR BEING NEITHER A RADISH NOR A HORSE. WHAT YOU ARE IS A LIAR FOOD.
-JIMMY FALLON

161. WHEN A TEACHER CALLS A BOY BY HIS ENTIRE NAME, IT MEANS TROUBLE.
-MARK TWAIN

162. I HAVE MADE UP MY MIND THAT I MUST HAVE MONEY, PA. I FEEL THAT I CAN'T BEG IT, BORROW IT, OR STEAL IT; AND SO I HAVE RESOLVED THAT I MUST MARRY IT.
-CHARLES DICKENS

163. IF AMERICA LEADS A BLESSED LIFE, THEN WHY DID GOD PUT ALL OF OUR OIL UNDER PEOPLE WHO HATE US?
-JON STEWART

164. IF TRUTH IS BEAUTY, HOW COME NO ONE HAS THEIR HAIR DONE IN THE LIBRARY?
-LILY TOMLIN

165. I LIKE A WOMAN WITH A HEAD ON HER SHOULDERS. I HATE NECKS.
-STEVE MARTIN

166. I HATE WHEN NEW PARENTS ASK WHO THE BABY LOOKS LIKE! IT WAS BORN 15 MINUTES AGO, IT LOOKS LIKE A POTATO.
-KEVIN HART

167. REMEMBER, WHEN YOU ARE DEAD, YOU DO NOT KNOW YOU ARE DEAD. IT IS ONLY PAINFUL FOR OTHERS. THE SAME APPLIES WHEN YOU ARE STUPID.
-RICKY GERVAIS

168. WHEN YOU'RE BORN YOU GET A TICKET TO THE FREAK SHOW. WHEN YOU'RE BORN IN AMERICA, YOU GET A FRONT ROW SEAT.
-GEORGE CARLIN

169. IF OUR FOUNDING FATHERS WANTED US TO CARE ABOUT THE REST OF THE WORLD, THEY WOULDN'T HAVE DECLARED THEIR INDEPENDENCE FROM IT.
-STEPHEN COLBERT

170. HALLOWEEN IS THE BEGINNING OF THE HOLIDAY SHOPPING SEASON. THAT'S FOR WOMEN. THE BEGINNING OF THE HOLIDAY SHOPPING SEASON FOR MEN IS CHRISTMAS EVE.
-DAVID LETTERMAN

171. WENT TO DISNEYLAND BECAUSE MY DAUGHTER'S OBSESSED WITH MICKEY MOUSE. SHE WAS SO EXCITED WHEN I GOT HOME AND TOLD HER.
-RYAN REYNOLDS

172. THE SECRET OF LIFE IS HONESTY AND FAIR DEALING. IF YOU CAN FAKE THAT, YOU'VE GOT IT MADE.
-GROUCHO MARX

173. A CLEAR CONSCIENCE IS USUALLY THE SIGN OF A BAD MEMORY.
-STEVEN WRIGHT

174. I AM NOT A MEMBER OF ANY ORGANIZED POLITICAL PARTY. I AM A DEMOCRAT.
-WILL ROGERS

175. I LOOKED UP MY FAMILY TREE AND FOUND OUT I WAS THE SAP.
-RODNEY DANGERFIELD

176. BREAST FEEDING ACTIVISTS PLAN TO DESCEND ON WASHINGTON FOR A PUBLIC BREAST FEEDING DEMONSTRATION. ALSO DESCENDING ON WASHINGTON, THOUSANDS OF MEN SAYING, "WHAT? I'M LOOKING AT THE BABY".
-CONAN O'BRIEN

177. MARRY A MAN YOUR OWN AGE; AS YOUR BEAUTY
FADES, SO WILL HIS EYESIGHT.
-PHYLLIS DILLER

178. IT HAS BEEN SAID THAT POLITICS IS THE
SECOND OLDEST PROFESSION. I HAVE LEARNED THAT
IT BEARS A STRIKING RESEMBLANCE TO THE FIRST.
-RONALD REAGAN

179. IF YOU WANT YOUR CHILDREN TO LISTEN, TRY
TALKING SOFTLY TO SOMEONE ELSE.
-ANN LANDERS

180. IF THE PEOPLE DON'T WANT TO COME OUT TO
THE BALLPARK, NOBODY'S GOING TO STOP THEM.
-YOGI BERRA

181. WHAT IS A DATE, REALLY, BUT A JOB
INTERVIEW THAT LASTS ALL NIGHT? THE ONLY
DIFFERENCE IS THAT IN NOT MANY JOB INTERVIEWS
IS THERE A CHANCE YOU'LL WIND UP NAKED.
-JERRY SEINFELD

182. I DIDN'T FAIL THE TEST. I JUST FOUND 100
WAYS TO DO IT WRONG.
-BENJAMIN FRANKLIN

183. CONFIDENCE IS WHAT YOU HAVE BEFORE YOU UNDERSTAND THE PROBLEM.
-WOODY ALLEN

184. IF YOU THINK YOU ARE TOO SMALL TO MAKE A DIFFERENCE, TRY SLEEPING WITH A MOSQUITO.
-DALAI LAMA

185. ALL OF US HAVE MOMENTS IN OUR LIVES THAT TEST OUR COURAGE. TAKING CHILDREN INTO A HOUSE WITH A WHITE CARPET IS ONE OF THEM.
-ERMA BOMBECK

186. SCIENTISTS NOW BELIEVE THAT THE PRIMARY BIOLOGICAL FUNCTION OF BREASTS IS TO MAKE MEN STUPID.
-DAVE BARRY

187. IF WOMEN RAN THE WORLD WE WOULDN'T HAVE WARS, JUST INTENSE NEGOTIATIONS EVERY 28 DAYS.
-ROBIN WILLIAMS

188. IF YOU ARE NOT YELLING AT YOUR KIDS, YOU ARE NOT SPENDING ENOUGH TIME WITH THEM.
-REESE WITHERSPOON

189. MY DEFINITION OF AN INTELLECTUAL IS SOMEONE WHO CAN LISTEN TO THE WILLIAM TELL OVERTURE WITHOUT THINKING OF THE LONE RANGER.
-BILLY CONNOLLY

190. PIE CAN'T COMPETE WITH CAKE. PUT CANDLES IN A CAKE, IT'S A BIRTHDAY CAKE. PUT CANDLES IN A PIE, AND SOMEBODY'S DRUNK IN THE KITCHEN.
-JIM GAFFIGAN

191. YOU KNOW THERE'S A PROBLEM WHEN YOU REALIZE THAT OUT OF THE THREE RS, ONLY ONE BEGINS WITH AN R.
-DENNIS MILLER

192. TRYING ON PANTS IS ONE OF THE MOST HUMILIATING THINGS A MAN CAN SUFFER THAT DOESN'T INVOLVE A WOMAN.
-LARRY DAVID

193. WOMEN MARRY MEN HOPING THEY WILL CHANGE. MEN MARRY WOMEN HOPING THEY WILL NOT. SO EACH IS INEVITABLY DISAPPOINTED.
-ALBERT EINSTEIN

194. I HAVE NOTICED THAT EVEN PEOPLE WHO CLAIM EVERYTHING IS PRE-DETERMINED AND THAT WE CAN DO NOTHING TO CHANGE IT LOOK BEFORE THEY CROSS THE ROAD.
-STEPHEN HAWKING

195. THE ONLY PEOPLE WHO STILL CALL HURRICANES ACTS OF GOD ARE THE PEOPLE WHO WRITE INSURANCE FORMS.
-NEIL DEGRASSE TYSON

196. MY ADVICE TO YOU IS GET MARRIED: IF YOU FIND A GOOD WIFE YOU'LL BE HAPPY; IF NOT, YOU'LL BECOME A PHILOSOPHER.
-SOCRATES

197. IF GOD WANTED US TO BEND OVER HE'D PUT DIAMONDS ON THE FLOOR.
-JOAN RIVERS

198. INSTEAD OF GETTING MARRIED AGAIN, I'M GOING TO FIND A WOMAN I DON'T LIKE AND JUST GIVE HER A HOUSE.
-ROD STEWART

199. GET YOUR FACTS FIRST, THEN YOU CAN DISTORT THEM AS YOU PLEASE.
-MARK TWAIN

200. FACEBOOK IS LIKE JAIL, YOU SIT AROUND AND WASTE TIME, YOU WRITE ON WALLS AND YOU GET POKED BY PEOPLE YOU DON'T KNOW.
-WILL FERRELL

201. PEOPLE ALWAYS ASK ME, "WERE YOU FUNNY AS A CHILD?" WELL, NO, I WAS AN ACCOUNTANT.
-ELLEN DEGENERES

202. I WAS GOING TO SUE FOR DEFAMATION OF CHARACTER, BUT THEN I REALIZED I HAVE NO CHARACTER.
-CHARLES BARKLEY

203. WHAT A KID I GOT, I TOLD HIM ABOUT THE BIRDS AND THE BEES AND HE TOLD ME ABOUT THE BUTCHER AND MY WIFE.
-RODNEY DANGERFIELD

204. IT'S JUST A JOB. GRASS GROWS, BIRDS FLY, WAVES POUND THE SAND. I BEAT PEOPLE UP.
-MUHAMMAD ALI

205. I HAVE WONDERED AT TIMES WHAT THE TEN COMMANDMENTS WOULD HAVE LOOKED LIKE IF MOSES HAD RUN THEM THROUGH THE US CONGRESS.
-RONALD REAGAN

206. A MAN IN LOVE IS LIKE A CLIPPED COUPON - IT'S TIME TO CASH IN.
-MAE WEST

207. CONTRARY TO WHAT PEOPLE MAY SAY, THERE'S NO UPPER LIMIT ON STUPIDITY.
-STEPHEN COLBERT

208. THE TROUBLE WITH SOME WOMEN IS THAT THEY GET ALL EXCITED ABOUT NOTHING, AND THEN THEY MARRY HIM.
-CHER

209. WHEN I EVENTUALLY MET MR. RIGHT I HAD NO IDEA THAT HIS FIRST NAME WAS ALWAYS.
-RITA RUDNER

210. THE DIFFERENCE BETWEEN FICTION AND REALITY? FICTION HAS TO MAKE SENSE.
-TOM CLANCY

211. HERE'S SOMETHING TO THINK ABOUT: HOW COME YOU NEVER SEE A HEADLINE LIKE "PSYCHIC WINS LOTTERY"?
-JAY LENO

212. DON'T SWEAT THE PETTY THINGS AND DON'T PET THE SWEATY THINGS.
-GEORGE CARLIN

213. I'M NOT OFFENDED BY BLONDE JOKES BECAUSE I KNOW I'M NOT DUMB ... AND I ALSO KNOW THAT I'M NOT BLONDE.
-DOLLY PARTON

214. I AM THANKFUL FOR LAUGHTER, EXCEPT WHEN MILK COMES OUT OF MY NOSE.
-WOODY ALLEN

215. GOOD GIRLS GO TO HEAVEN, BAD GIRLS GO EVERYWHERE.
-HELEN GURLEY BROWN

216. HE HAS NO ENEMIES, BUT IS INTENSELY DISLIKED BY HIS FRIENDS.
-OSCAR WILDE

217. THE TROUBLE WITH THIS COUNTRY IS THAT THERE ARE TOO MANY PEOPLE GOING ABOUT SAYING, "THE TROUBLE WITH THIS COUNTRY IS …"
-SINCLAIR LEWIS

218. I ONLY DRINK CHAMPAGNE ON TWO OCCASIONS, WHEN I AM IN LOVE AND WHEN I AM NOT.
-COCO CHANEL

219. KNOWLEDGE IS LIKE UNDERWEAR. IT IS USEFUL TO HAVE IT, BUT NOT NECESSARY TO SHOW IT OFF.
-BILL MURRAY

220. BASEBALL IS 90% MENTAL AND THE OTHER HALF IS PHYSICAL.
-YOGI BERRA

221. YOU CAN LEAD A MAN TO CONGRESS, BUT YOU CAN'T MAKE HIM THINK.
-MILTON BERLE

222. THOSE ARE MY PRINCIPLES, AND IF YOU DON'T LIKE THEM... WELL I HAVE OTHERS.
-GROUCHO MARX

223 HOW MANY PEOPLE HERE HAVE TELEKENETIC POWERS? RAISE MY HAND.
-EMO PHILIPS

224. A LOT OF PEOPLE ARE AFRAID OF HEIGHTS. NOT ME, I'M AFRAID OF WIDTHS.
-STEVEN WRIGHT

225. THE CATHOLIC CHURCH HAS APPROVED A NEW APP THAT LETS YOU MAKE CONFESSIONS OVER YOUR IPHONE. IT ALSO RAISES THE POSSIBILITY OF ACCIDENTALLY BUTT-DIALING GOD.
-CONAN O'BRIEN

226. THERE IS THE VEGETARIAN HOT POCKET FOR THOSE OF US WHO DON'T WANT TO EAT MEAT, BUT WOULD STILL LIKE DIARRHEA.
-JIM GAFFIGAN

227. THE BEST MEASURE OF A MAN'S HONESTY ISN'T HIS INCOME TAX RETURN. IT'S THE ZERO ADJUST ON HIS BATHROOM SCALE.
-ARTHUR C. CLARKE

228. I NEVER EXPECTED TO SEE THE DAY WHEN GIRLS WOULD GET SUNBURNED IN THE PLACES THEY NOW DO.
-WILL ROGERS

229. MARRIAGE IS A WONDERFUL INSTITUTION, BUT WHO WOULD WANT TO LIVE IN AN INSTITUTION?
-H. L. MENCKEN

230. MY FAKE PLANTS DIED BECAUSE I DID NOT PRETEND TO WATER THEM.
-MITCH HEDBERG

231. HAPPINESS IS HAVING A LARGE, LOVING, CARING, CLOSE-KNIT FAMILY IN ANOTHER CITY.
-GEORGE BURNS

232. BE CAREFUL ABOUT READING HEALTH BOOKS.
YOU MAY DIE OF A MISPRINT.
-MARK TWAIN

233. I HAVEN'T SPOKEN TO MY WIFE IN YEARS. I
DIDN'T WANT TO INTERRUPT HER.
-RODNEY DANGERFIELD

234. LIFE DOESN'T IMITATE ART, IT IMITATES BAD
TELEVISION.
-WOODY ALLEN

235. YOU KNOW YOU'RE GETTING OLD WHEN YOU GET
THAT ONE CANDLE ON THE CAKE. IT'S LIKE, "SEE
IF YOU CAN BLOW THIS OUT".
-JERRY SEINFELD

236. A LIE GETS HALFWAY AROUND THE WORLD
BEFORE THE TRUTH HAS A CHANCE TO GET ITS PANTS
ON.
-WINSTON CHURCHILL

237. IF I HAD TO LIVE MY LIFE OVER, I'D LIVE
OVER A SALOON.
-W. C. FIELDS

238. THOMAS JEFFERSON ONCE SAID, "WE SHOULD NEVER JUDGE A PRESIDENT BY HIS AGE, ONLY BY HIS WORKS." AND EVER SINCE HE TOLD ME THAT, I STOPPED WORRYING.
-RONALD REAGAN

239. I DON'T LIKE TO BE OUT OF MY COMFORT ZONE, WHICH IS ABOUT A HALF AN INCH WIDE.
-LARRY DAVID

240. THE PEN IS MIGHTIER THAN THE SWORD, IF YOU SHOOT THAT PEN OUT OF A GUN.
-STEPHEN COLBERT

241. I LOVE MICKEY MOUSE MORE THAN ANY WOMAN I HAVE EVER KNOWN.
-WALT DISNEY

242. IF I WERE TWO-FACED, WOULD I BE WEARING THIS ONE?
-ABRAHAM LINCOLN

243. I BUY EXPENSIVE SUITS. THEY JUST LOOK CHEAP ON ME.
-WARREN BUFFETT

244. TRYING TO BE HAPPY BY ACCUMULATING POSSESSIONS IS LIKE TRYING TO SATISFY HUNGER BY TAPING SANDWICHES ALL OVER YOUR BODY.
-GEORGE CARLIN

245. I HAVE A WONDERFUL MAKE-UP CREW. THEY'RE THE SAME PEOPLE RESTORING THE STATUE OF LIBERTY.
-BOB HOPE

246. I'M GOING TO MARRY A JEWISH WOMAN BECAUSE I LIKE THE IDEA OF GETTING UP SUNDAY MORNING AND GOING TO THE DELI.
-MICHAEL J. FOX

247. I DON'T LOOK LIKE HALLE BERRY. BUT CHANCES ARE, SHE'S GOING TO END UP LOOKING LIKE ME.
-WHOOPI GOLDBERG

248. FIRST THE DOCTOR TOLD ME THE GOOD NEWS: I WAS GOING TO HAVE A DISEASE NAMED AFTER ME.
-STEVE MARTIN

249. NEVER UNDER ANY CIRCUMSTANCES TAKE A SLEEPING PILL AND A LAXATIVE ON THE SAME NIGHT.
-DAVE BARRY

250. I WANT MY CHILDREN TO HAVE ALL THE THINGS I COULDN'T AFFORD. THEN I WANT TO MOVE IN WITH THEM.
-PHYLLIS DILLER

251. IF AT FIRST YOU DON'T SUCCEED... SO MUCH FOR SKYDIVING.
-HENNY YOUNGMAN

252. I LOVE DEADLINES. I LIKE THE WHOOSHING SOUND THEY MAKE AS THEY FLY BY.
-DOUGLAS ADAMS

253. IF LOVE IS THE ANSWER, COULD YOU PLEASE REPHRASE THE QUESTION?
-LILY TOMLIN

254. THE TOWELS WERE SO THICK THERE I COULD HARDLY CLOSE MY SUITCASE.
-YOGI BERRA

255. ANY GIRL CAN BE GLAMOROUS. ALL YOU HAVE TO DO IS STAND STILL AND LOOK STUPID.
-HEDY LAMARR

256. YOU KNOW YOU MUST BE DOING SOMETHING RIGHT IF OLD PEOPLE LIKE YOU.
-DAVE CHAPPELLE

257. LEARN FROM THE MISTAKES OF OTHERS. YOU CAN NEVER LIVE LONG ENOUGH TO MAKE THEM ALL YOURSELF.
-GROUCHO MARX

258. YOU SEE MUCH MORE OF YOUR CHILDREN ONCE THEY LEAVE HOME.
-LUCILLE BALL

259. EVER WONDER WHAT PEOPLE GOT JESUS FOR CHRISTMAS? IT'S LIKE, "OH GREAT, SOCKS. YOU KNOW I'M DYING FOR YOUR SINS RIGHT? YEAH, BUT THANKS FOR THE SOCKS! THEY'LL GO GREAT WITH MY SANDALS."
-JIM GAFFIGAN

260. I HAVE A NEW PHILOSOPHY. I'M ONLY GOING TO DREAD ONE DAY AT A TIME.
-CHARLES M. SCHULZ

261. I USED TO JOG BUT THE ICE CUBES KEPT FALLING OUT OF MY GLASS.
-DAVID LEE ROTH

262. I'M LIKE OLD WINE. THEY DON'T BRING ME OUT VERY OFTEN - BUT I'M WELL PRESERVED.
-ROSE KENNEDY

263. WHEN YOU ARE COURTING A NICE GIRL AN HOUR SEEMS LIKE A SECOND. WHEN YOU SIT ON A RED-HOT CINDER A SECOND SEEMS LIKE AN HOUR. THAT'S RELATIVITY.
-ALBERT EINSTEIN

264. THE ODDS OF GOING TO THE STORE FOR A LOAF OF BREAD AND COMING OUT WITH ONLY A LOAF OF BREAD ARE THREE BILLION TO ONE.
-ERMA BOMBECK

265. SOMEONE ASKED ME, IF I WERE STRANDED ON A DESERT ISLAND WHAT BOOK WOULD I BRING… "HOW TO BUILD A BOAT."
-STEVEN WRIGHT

266. MY GRANDMOTHER STARTED WALKING FIVE MILES A DAY WHEN SHE WAS SIXTY. SHE'S NINETY-SEVEN NOW, AND WE DON'T KNOW WHERE THE HELL SHE IS.
-ELLEN DEGENERES

267. BEHIND EVERY GREAT MAN IS A WOMAN ROLLING HER EYES.
-JIM CARREY

268. LIVE EVERYDAY AS IF IT WERE YOUR LAST BECAUSE SOMEDAY YOU'RE GOING TO BE RIGHT.
-MUHAMMAD ALI

269. CANDY CORN IS THE ONLY CANDY IN THE HISTORY OF AMERICA THAT'S NEVER BEEN ADVERTISED. AND THERE'S A REASON. ALL OF THE CANDY CORN THAT WAS EVER MADE WAS MADE IN 1911.
-LEWIS BLACK

270. THE DIFFERENCE BETWEEN SEX AND LOVE IS THAT SEX RELIEVES TENSION AND LOVE CAUSES IT.
-WOODY ALLEN

271. BETWEEN TWO EVILS, I ALWAYS PICK THE ONE I NEVER TRIED BEFORE.
-MAE WEST

272. I WAS SO NAIVE AS A KID I USED TO SNEAK BEHIND THE BARN AND DO NOTHING.
-JOHNNY CARSON

273. MEN ARE LIARS. WE'LL LIE ABOUT LYING IF WE HAVE TO. I'M AN ALGEBRA LIAR. I FIGURE TWO GOOD LIES MAKE A POSITIVE.
-TIM ALLEN

274. BEFORE I REFUSE TO TAKE YOUR QUESTIONS, I HAVE AN OPENING STATEMENT.
-RONALD REAGAN

275. MY MOTHER WAS AGAINST ME BEING AN ACTRESS - UNTIL I INTRODUCED HER TO FRANK SINATRA.
-ANGIE DICKINSON

276. IF IT'S THE PSYCHIC NETWORK WHY DO THEY NEED A PHONE NUMBER?
-ROBIN WILLIAMS

277. THE FIRST TIME I SANG IN THE CHURCH CHOIR TWO HUNDRED PEOPLE CHANGED THEIR RELIGION.
-FRED ALLEN

278. ALCOHOL IS LIKE PHOTOSHOP FOR REAL LIFE.
-WILL FERRELL

279. WE SLEEP IN SEPARATE ROOMS, WE HAVE DINNER APART, WE TAKE SEPARATE VACATIONS - WE'RE DOING EVERYTHING WE CAN TO KEEP OUR MARRIAGE TOGETHER.
-RODNEY DANGERFIELD

280. TO LOSE ONE PARENT MAY BE REGARDED AS A MISFORTUNE; TO LOSE BOTH LOOKS LIKE CARELESSNESS.
-OSCAR WILDE

281. THE ONE THING YOU SHOULDN'T DO IS TRY TO TELL A CAB DRIVER HOW TO GET SOMEWHERE.
-JIMMY FALLON

282. UKRAINE ANNOUNCED PLANS TO OPEN CHERNOBYL, THEIR NUCLEAR DISASTER SITE, TO TOURISTS. THEY SAY IT'S JUST LIKE DISNEYLAND, EXCEPT THE 6-FOOT MOUSE IS REAL.
-CONAN O'BRIEN

283. ISN'T IT A BIT UNNERVING THAT DOCTORS CALL WHAT THEY DO "PRACTICE"?
-GEORGE CARLIN

284. DON'T FORGET MOTHER'S DAY. OR AS THEY CALL IT IN BEVERLY HILLS, DAD'S THIRD WIFE DAY.
-JAY LENO

285. AS A CHILD MY FAMILY'S MENU CONSISTED OF TWO CHOICES: TAKE IT OR LEAVE IT.
-BUDDY HACKETT

286. I WAS GRATIFIED TO BE ABLE TO ANSWER PROMPTLY, AND I DID. I SAID I DIDN'T KNOW.
-MARK TWAIN

287. EVERY MAN'S DREAM IS TO BE ABLE TO SINK INTO THE ARMS OF A WOMAN WITHOUT ALSO FALLING INTO HER HANDS.
-JERRY LEWIS

288. I DON'T KNOW (IF THEY WERE MEN OR WOMEN FANS RUNNING NAKED ACROSS THE FIELD). THEY HAD BAGS OVER THEIR HEADS.
-YOGI BERRA

289. WE OWE A LOT TO THOMAS EDISON - IF IT WASN'T FOR HIM, WE'D BE WATCHING TELEVISION BY CANDLELIGHT.
-MILTON BERLE

290. EVERYTHING IS FUNNY, AS LONG AS IT'S HAPPENING TO SOMEBODY ELSE.
-WILL ROGERS

291. IT'S A FUNNY THING THAT WHEN A MAN HASN'T ANYTHING ON EARTH TO WORRY ABOUT, HE GOES OFF AND GETS MARRIED.
-ROBERT FROST

292. A DATE IS AN EXPERIENCE YOU HAVE WITH ANOTHER PERSON THAT MAKES YOU APPRECIATE BEING ALONE.
-LARRY DAVID

293. MY WIFE AND I WERE HAPPY FOR TWENTY YEARS. THEN WE MET.
-RODNEY DANGERFIELD

294. YOU KNOW YOU'VE REACHED MIDDLE AGE WHEN YOU'RE CAUTIONED TO SLOW DOWN BY YOUR DOCTOR, INSTEAD OF BY THE POLICE.
-JOAN RIVERS

295. THE INTERNET IS JUST A WORLD PASSING NOTES AROUND A CLASSROOM.
-JON STEWART

296. I NEVER FORGET A FACE - BUT IN YOUR CASE, I'LL BE GLAD TO MAKE AN EXCEPTION.
-GROUCHO MARX

297. MONDAYS ARE FINE. IT'S YOUR LIFE THAT SUCKS.
-RICKY GERVAIS

298. MEN WANT THE SAME THING FROM THEIR UNDERWEAR THAT THEY WANT FROM WOMEN: A LITTLE BIT OF SUPPORT, AND A LITTLE BIT OF FREEDOM.
-JERRY SEINFELD

299. I WAS SLEEPING THE OTHER NIGHT, ALONE, THANKS TO THE EXTERMINATOR.
-EMO PHILIPS

300. I'M NOT A PERSON WHO EMBRACES CHALLENGES. I RUN FROM CHALLENGES. I BREAK WORLD RECORDS RUNNING FROM CHALLENGES. -LARRY DAVID

THANK YOU!

Please leave us a review on Amazon.

Amazon reviews are very
important to our business and
help other puzzle lovers find
our books.

Please go to this book on Amazon
and let us know your honest
opinion.

It would mean the world to us.
Thank you!

Don't forget to sign up to our
VIP Newsletter to get all of our
future releases absolutely free!
www.gamenest.org/free

Made in the USA
Las Vegas, NV
22 November 2022